UNDERSTANDING RHETORIC

2nd Edition

a GRAPHIC GUIDE to WRITING

for Eastern Michigan University

Elizabeth Losh
Jonathan Alexander
Kevin Cannon
Zander Cannon

macmillan learning
curriculum solutions

Manufactured in the United States of America.
2 1 0 9 8 7
f e d c b a

For information, write: Curriculum Solutions, 14903 Pilot Drive, Plymouth, MI 48170
  (macmillanlearning.com)

ISBN 978-1-319-13087-9 (Eastern Michigan University edition)

Welcome to
Eastern Michigan University

As directors of the First-Year Writing Program, we invite you to compose, experiment, reflect, and learn with your peers and your instructor in the program's small, studio-based classes. Whether or not you are immediately aware of it, you have had a long history as a reader and writer. Every day we compose text messages, e-mails, digital status updates, memos, lists, and notes. We read signs, blogs, phones, magazines, advertisements, pamphlets, books, and more. Since we each come to the classroom with these different experiences as literate individuals, the goal of the First-Year Writing Program's two-course sequence is to amplify and build upon this rich diversity through thoughtful interaction, guided project development, and continuous reflection. Further, the course sequence helps you gain experience in and confidence with different composing situations, or rhetorical contexts, and prepares you for writing throughout your academic and professional life by encouraging conscious, thoughtful responses to the compositions you create and confront.

You are already a member of numerous communities—groups that form around particular practices and identifications related to arts, sports, values, or locations. The First-Year Writing Program course sequence encourages you to become more aware of how these communities operate, as you are at the same time welcomed to a new discourse community, that of the university. Because of the small, personal nature of first-year writing courses, we hope that in addition to providing you a solid foundation for writing at the university, you're introduced to a cohort of people to whom you can turn throughout your time at EMU. Your instructor and classmates will be invested in your ideas, your writing development, and your ultimate academic success at EMU. In each class you take at the university, you will be asked to compose in different contexts, in different formats, and for different audiences. Although the First-Year Writing Program's two-course sequence cannot introduce you to every writing genre you may come across in your time at EMU, we can provide you with the tools to approach different writing contexts. We do this through a focus on how compositions answer to a particular rhetorical context or event, and together we examine the recursive process through which we

Derek N. Mueller,
*Director of the First-Year
Writing Program and Associate
Professor of Written Communication*

approach these different events: the questioning, inventing, composing, arranging, revising, reflecting, and reworking. The pages that follow are meant to briefly introduce you to the First-Year Writing Program course sequence so that you begin the semester with a sense of the program's design and its dedication to helping you gain a strong start in college. Here you will find program principles, course outcomes, recommendations for success in your courses, and selected guidelines and policies. Throughout, you'll also find callout boxes featuring specific advice from students, information about university resources and support services, and questions for discussion and reflection. If you have questions about this guide, the course text, or the program, you're invited to meet with us. We hope that the semester brings you challenges, surprises, and success.

DISCUSSION QUESTIONS

1. Which communities do you belong to?
2. Have you ever been in a class or academic setting that felt like a community?
3. How do you think of that community in terms of language practices?

First-Year Writing Program at Eastern Michigan University

FIRST-YEAR WRITING PROGRAM

Introductory Courses

Early in an undergraduate program of study, many students take introductory courses, which are designed to lay a foundation for more advanced studies. Introductory courses also reinforce and build upon lessons learned in high school, and they refresh important habits, practices, and ways of knowing that may have gone untended for a few years. The first-year writing courses at EMU are sequenced to provide students with a foundation in college-level reading and writing practices (WRTG 120) and advanced research and writing skills customarily practiced in upper division courses and in majors offered at the university (WRTG 121).

> ### DISCUSSION QUESTIONS
> 1. What are your expectations for writing at the college level?
> 2. On what experiences and/or conversations are these expectations based?
> 3. How much writing do you think you'll be asked to do in your major? In your future career?

The First-Year Writing Program Two-Course Sequence

Because writing will be integral to your success at Eastern Michigan University and beyond, the First-Year Writing Program (FYWP) curriculum is designed as a two-course sequence. Many students take WRTG 120, Composition 1: Writing the College Experience, in the fall of their first year and WRTG 121, Composition 2: Researching the Public Experience, in the winter of their first year. The primary purpose of the sequence is to provide students with focused and sustained instruction in writing. Writing is a cornerstone of the effective communication habits and skills you will use to be successful within your field of study both at the university level and within the workplace. WRTG 120 introduces principles of effective written communication, and WRTG 121 builds on this foundation, encouraging sophisticated rhetorical performance and thoughtful reflection involving research.

Course Descriptions

WRTG 120—Composition I: Writing the College Experience *(3 credits)* Introduces use of writing and reading for inquiry. Students write extended essays about subjects relevant to the college experience using conventions of Standard Written English; assignments may also incorporate other genres and styles. Emphasis is placed on using writing and reading as a process for discovery, and on communicating ideas to audiences.

WRTG 121—Composition II: Researching the Public Experience *(3 credits)* Focuses on academic writing and inquiry. Students use multiple modes of research to develop literacy used in academic and other public contexts. Through extended reading and writing, students engage in the process of writing researched essays that reflect conventions of Standard Written English and standard documentation styles.

WRTG 121, Composition II: Researching the Public Experience, is part of the EMU General Education Program's Effective Communication area. In WRTG 121, EMU students develop the foundation for writing, research, and critical thinking strategies that they will use throughout their college careers and in the workplace. Writing is both a means of communication and a tool for developing new ideas. Good writers are flexible. They know how to assess the expectations of a variety of audiences with whom they want to communicate and how to draw on or develop different strategies to meet those expectations. Good writers also understand that different kinds of writing have different conventions and they can move fluidly between those conventions. WRTG 121 students develop these strategies that are key to effective communication throughout the course. Students write between fifty and seventy pages of draft work and between twenty and thiry pages of polished, final-draft work during the course of the semester, and that work is supported and directed by frequent feedback from the instructor.

Five Key Principles and Course Outcomes

Five key principles guide instruction in EMU's First-Year Writing Program: rhetoric, process, conventions, multimodality, and reflection. You will hear more about each of these principles throughout the semester, and your instructor will often reiterate these concepts during in-class activities, in writing assignments, and in evaluations of your work. But we consider these principles to be farther-reaching than any one class or sequence of classes, even farther-reaching than an undergraduate degree program. The five principles will persist long after you graduate and will prove a reliable resource in many communication situations in personal, professional, and civic life. Scholars in writing studies have recently identified principles like these as *threshold concepts*, or as principles that both anchor a domain of knowledge and, once learned, cannot be unlearned. In other words, as you gain focal experience with these principles in first-year writing, you are forming foundational habits, practices, and ways of thinking that will transfer to communicating effectively in many other situations.

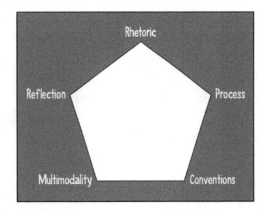

1. **Rhetoric:** Communication practices that are self-aware about making a purposeful impression and affecting change in diverse situations

2. **Process:** The ways in which effective communication builds up and is developed in time

3. **Conventions:** Predictable, loosely rule-governed patterns in communication, which are generally agreed upon within academic communities

4. **Multimodality:** Composition that engages with a wide range of materials and is both intensified and complicated by writing in digital environments

5. **Reflection:** When writers pause, take stock, and look back at what has worked well, what might have been handled differently, and the ways such insights inform future communication

Because each of these five principles refers to a complex array of issues, brief but adequate definitions are difficult to establish. Nevertheless, we consider the definitions listed above to be useful for beginning the conversation about each principle. As your studies progress, you will begin to notice important additions

DISCUSSION QUESTIONS

1. How do these five concepts operate in specific writing you have done before?
2. Have you come across these concepts in different contexts? What are some of them?
3. How might you paraphrase these concepts, putting them into your own words?

and qualifications that add depth, subtlety, and texture to these preliminary definitions.

FYWP Two-Course Sequence Outcomes[1]

Principles	WRTG 120 Focus	WRTG 121 Focus
Rhetoric	Rhetorical knowledge	Rhetorical performance
Process	Writing process	Research process
Conventions	Genre conventions	Style conventions
Multimodality	Multimodal transformation	Multimodal design
Reflection	Reflective practice	Reflective interaction

Table 1. Program Principles and Course Outcomes.

Table 1 lists the five key principles for the First-Year Writing Program as each relates to a specific course outcome in WRTG 120 and WRTG 121. The principle in column one provides a broader frame in relation to the specific outcomes listed in columns two and three, respectively. The table also indicates the sequential relationship between outcomes in the two courses as they are linked by the cohering principle. Outcomes specified for WRTG 121 and listed in column three in effect build upon outcomes specified for WRTG 120 and listed in column two.

---

[1] EMU's First-Year Writing Program outcomes have been adapted from the Council of Writing Program Administrators (CWPA) "Outcomes Statement for First-Year Composition" (2008) and the "Framework for Success in Postsecondary Writing" (2011), which was jointly developed by the CWPA, the National Council of Teachers of English, and the National Writing Project.

WRTG 120 Outcomes and Key Concepts

Principles and Outcomes	Description
Rhetorical knowledge	You will have practiced using language consciously and identifying rhetorical qualities in composing situations.
Writing process	You will have engaged in invention, drafting, and rewriting, providing explicit evidence of a writing process.
Genre conventions	You will have demonstrated awareness of academic writing genre conventions, including mechanics and syntax.
Multimodal transformation	You will have adapted your writing to distinct rhetorical contexts, drawing attention to the way composition transforms across contexts and forms.
Reflective practice	You will have applied feedback from instructor, peers, and individual reflection to rethink, re-see, and ultimately revise your work.

Table 2. Program Principles and WRTG 120 Outcomes.

Table 2 shows the relationship between the five key principles, the specific course outcomes for WRTG 120, and the brief descriptions of each outcome. The five WRTG 121 course outcomes also serve as EMU's General Education Outcomes for Area I: Effective Communication.

The five course outcomes for WRTG 120 indicate the priorities guiding instruction, assignment design, and the general progression of the class. You will be asked to reflect upon the connections you find between the five outcomes, selected projects, and your portfolio. The outcomes focus and organize the class, but there are numerous additional dimensions to the class, including considerations of literacy development, critical reading strategies, genre awareness, and practice with language conventions, including syntax and mechanics. We mention this because, while the outcomes serve as beacons to guide the class, a first-year writing class involves much more, some of which is collected in the word cloud on the next page.

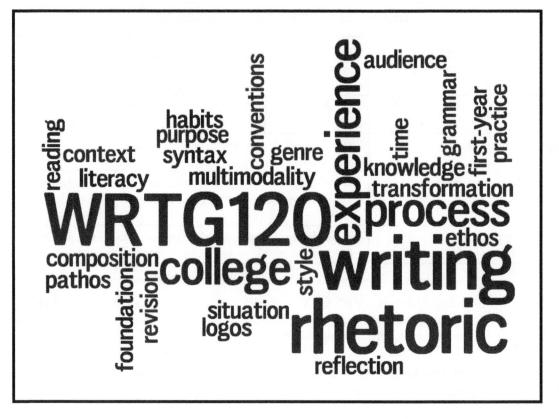

Figure 1. WRTG 120 Word Cloud.

(Created by Eastern Michigan University via Wordle.net.)

In addition to the course outcomes, WRTG 120 addresses many foundational habits, practices, and concepts pertinent to writing in college and beyond. See Figure 1 above: this word cloud represents some of them.

WRTG 121 Outcomes and Key Concepts

Principles and Outcomes	Description
Rhetorical performance	You will have enacted rhetoric by consciously constructing persuasive texts.
Research process	You will have practiced different research methods, which include analyzing and using sources and developing primary research.
Style conventions	You will have developed awareness of conventions of academic research processes, including documentation systems and their purposes.
Multimodal design	You will have composed using digital technologies, gaining awareness of the possibilities and constraints of electronic environments.
Reflective interaction	You will have shared your work with your instructor, peers, and/or the university community and accounted for the impact of such interaction on composition.

Table 3. Program Principles and WRTG 121 Outcomes.

Table 3 shows the relationship between the five key principles, the specific course outcomes for WRTG 121, and the brief descriptions of each outcome.

Much the same as with WRTG 120, the five explicit outcomes for WRTG 121 provide a distinct organizing frame for the class. The outcomes will be focal at many moments throughout the semester, especially when you write reflections on the projects you have completed or in your final portfolio. Yet, because we don't want to overload the outcomes or burden them with naming every minor aspect of the class, we want to openly acknowledge that there is much more to the class than these five outcomes. The content of these classes is writing, but we understand that a foundation for successful writing includes critical reading, rhetorical listening, speaking, multimodal design and representation, and working in digital environments. In addition to the five outcomes, the word cloud on the next page highlights additional dimensions of WRTG 121.

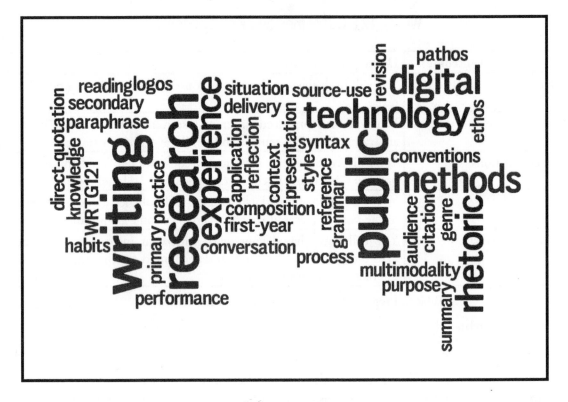

Figure 2. WRTG 121 Word Cloud.

(Created by Eastern Michigan University via Wordle.net.)

In addition to the course outcomes, WRTG 121 incorporates many other strategies and techniques salient to researched academic writing in the twenty-first century. See Figure 2 above: this word cloud represents some of them.

Written Communication at Eastern Michigan University

The First-Year Writing Program is the first place students at EMU will take a writing class, but Composition I and Composition II are only a small part of the EMU landscape when it comes to writing. Several other classes at EMU build upon the first-year writing experience, drawing on similar concepts, habits, and practices in what we would describe as a vertical curriculum. A vertical writing curriculum operates according to the idea that students ought to have focused experiences with writing every semester. Writing is a generalizable skill that matters greatly in all aspects of personal, professional, and civic life.

We are fortunate at EMU to offer a Written Communication Major and a Writing Minor. Students in both of these programs are assured small classes with faculty who care deeply about guiding them through a wide variety of writing projects. One of the core ideas in the Written Communication Major and Writing Minor is that theory and practice are intertwined, with each feeding into and constituting the other. Practice informs theory and theory informs practice, endlessly, and many of the programs' courses and projects draw upon this principle.

WRTG Classes That Follow from WRTG 121

If you value the practices, habits, and learning you gain from your first-year writing class, consider enrolling in any of the following courses to gain a stronger sense of whether the Written Communication Major or Writing Minor might be of interest to you:

WRTG 225: Writing in a Changing World *(3 credits)*

WRTG 310: Writing and Civic Literacy *(3 credits)*

WRTG 323W: Writing in the Professional World *(3 credits)*

WRTG 324W: Principles of Technical Communication *(3 credits)*

WRTG 326: Research Writing *(3 credits)*

WRTG 354: Critical Digital Literacies *(3 credits)*

To learn more about the Written Communication Major or the Writing Minor, visit the Written Communication Web site at **emich.edu/english/programs/written-communication,** or contact the program coordinator for more information or to schedule an informal advising appointment:

Program Coordinator	Dr. Steven Krause
Office/Campus Address	612 Pray-Harrold (6th Floor)
Phone Number	(734) 487-0985
E-mail Address	skrause@emich.edu

Writing Intensive Classes at EMU

As a cornerstone of the General Education Program, every academic major at Eastern Michigan University includes a required Writing Intensive (WI) class. Students usually enroll in 300- or 400-level Writing Intensive classes after completing 60 or more credit hours (i.e., in their junior or senior year). With this in mind, the First-Year Writing Program plays an important role in preparing you with skills, knowledge, and habits that will have bearing on your success in future classes.

How to Succeed in the First-Year Writing Program and Beyond

Whether you have been in college for a few semesters or whether this is your first semester, revisiting patterns reflected in the habits of successful students often serves as a helpful reminder. We consider the following list of recommendations to be generally consistent with habits we have observed among successful students in the program and in the university more generally.

Read your syllabus. No, really, read it. Read it on the first day of class. Read it a second time carefully and completely by the end of the first week of class. Why should you read it more than once? The syllabus is the primary framing document for the entire semester. In it, you will find many answers to your questions. In fact, we would even go so far as to encourage you to read the syllabus thoroughly again at the end of the fourth week of classes and yet another  time around the middle of the semester. Get to know the syllabus well. It provides crucial information for being successful in the class. Office hours, contact information, important due dates, and specific policies are all outlined within a course syllabus. When in doubt, consult the syllabus. When you have questions about the syllabus, ask your instructor.

Attend class. Consistent, on-time attendance is essential to your success in first-year writing and in college. Those who show up and who show up on time are far more likely to have a grasp on pacing and workload related to a project, on the expectations of the instructor, and on the activities that reinforce key approaches to the gradual build-up of the class. In-class time cannot be reconstructed or made up. And, above all, learning in discourse communities requires presence. That is, communities cease to work in quite the same way when you are away or when you are completing tasks independent of the classroom interactions with your peers and your instructor. The First-Year Writing Program stands behind the Department of English Language and Literature attendance policy, and, as such, "students who do not participate regularly should expect to receive lower grades in the course," and "students who

> "Come to class every day and don't be late."
> —EMU Student

miss more than the equivalent of two weeks of class should consider withdrawing and taking the class in a future semester."

Bring your books. The First-Year Writing Program requires two books for all students: *EasyWriter* and *Understanding Rhetoric*. Bring these books to class daily. They are cornerstones of the curriculum, and, as such, successful students will interact with them frequently, both in and out of class. *EasyWriter* is a handbook that provides practical guidelines for many aspects of writing, from process basics to formatting and structural considerations. We believe it to be a resource that will serve you well in all of your college classes. *Understanding Rhetoric* is a primer in rhetorical concepts. Based on input from students just like you and from the program's instructional staff, we believe its graphic format is smart, fun, and engaging. Both books provide a foundation for your success with writing in college and beyond.

Check your electronic devices. Mobile technologies such as smartphones, laptops, and tablets are easy to carry in and out of classes. When used responsibly, they can be powerful complements to annotation, allow for Web-based lookups (e.g., of definitions or reference materials), and offer ready access to supplemental readings available as PDFs or on the Web. *But.* These technologies oftentimes divide our attention. With this in mind, we urge you to heed your own habits of interacting with electronic devices as well as to know and honor the specific policies set in place by your instructor. Most classes include a managed use policy in the syllabus. If you have any doubts about whether you are using a mobile technology responsibly, ask your instructor. If you use a mobile technology in a way that disrupts the class, your instructor may ask you to surrender the device for the duration of class. Repeated disruptive uses of mobile technologies may be regarded more seriously by the university. All of this is to say that successful students pause and check their use of devices in classes. You should, too.

E-mail with care. Frequent access to your Eagle e-mail account matters for your prospective success at Eastern Michigan University. Please check your e-mail account daily throughout the semester. Course changes, updates and announcements, and other campus information will reach you primarily via e-mail. It is fine if you have another, personal e-mail account, but, in such cases, you should either have your Eagle mail forwarded to your personal account or check Eagle mail frequently. Be mindful when you send e-mails, and consider your audience. Compose concise, formal messages when sending e-mail to instructors. Your instructor considers your e-mail message important and will respond to e-mails within a reasonable and appropriate amount of time, but make sure you've composed responsible, complete e-mails. As a general rule, allow 24-48 hours for a response, not including weekends. If more than four days pass without a response, consider following up with a second message to reiterate your question, or seek your instructor out during office hours.

STUDENT SUGGESTIONS FOR E-MAILING PROFESSORS

- Always include a specific subject line and the prefix and number for your course.
- Begin your message with an opening address or salutation (e.g., "Dear Professor Mueller"), and end your message with an appropriate closing (e.g., "Sincerely").
- Reflect a reasonable degree of care in your e-mails; use paragraphs, and proofread before sending.
- Make sure your professor is willing to accept assignments via e-mail before submitting them that way. (If you do submit an assignment this way, clearly label your e-mail, and include a message as well.)

Keep all of your work. The First-Year Writing Program uses a portfolio-based approach to assessment, which means that your success depends upon your keeping all copies of your work throughout the semester. Keep drafts, annotated copies, daily homework, and in-class writing. Keep everything. Gather it in a folder, and keep it organized. Keeping track of your writing in this way applies to digital copies, too. It is a good idea to back up your work. There are several free and easy ways to do this using cloud-based services, such as Google Drive or Dropbox, and inexpensive alternatives, such as USB drives. Lost or misplaced work can be a serious setback, one we hope you don't experience. Taking a few steps to gather and back up your work systematically will prove exceedingly helpful when major projects are due, and again at the end of the semester.

Manage your time. Time is slippery, especially during your first year of college. Although it is easy to overlook a due date, it is never acceptable, and missing one draft can make an entire project difficult to get back on track. Plan accordingly. Successful students keep calendars or planners. They enter reminders into scheduling systems, such as Google Calendar. They plan ahead. College is

> "Pace yourself. It really will not benefit you in any way to procrastinate 'til the night before something is due."
> —EMU Student

challenging enough without discovering deadlines at the last minute and scrambling to meet them. Because we want you to be successful, we want you to notice the vital importance of time management to your success.

Sleep. The first year of college can be exciting, especially at EMU with so many fun goings-on. Activity and noise might seem a constant, and it is easy to make trade-offs, such as staying up late for a Netflix marathon (because it *is* fun!). But you need rest. Your success in college this year and beyond depends upon sufficient rest. This may seem like an obvious one, but *seriously*, sleep. Yawning frequently or putting your head down in class is never okay. It can be distracting to your peers, and it is disrespectful to anyone who is trying to speak to you or interact with you about your work. Writing can be challenging, but all coursework can seem insurmountable without sleep. Make sure to take six to eight hours every night to recharge. Your well-being requires this much rest. And your success in college and in the First-year Writing Program sequence is nearly impossible without it.

Know your peers. Many of your peers are making the same adjustments to college that you are. Peer interaction is a substantial part of the First-Year Writing Program. Learning and writing are social acts, and small classes make it all the more likely that you will interact with and learn the 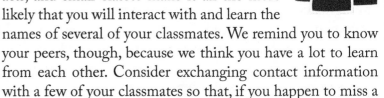 names of several of your classmates. We remind you to know your peers, though, because we think you have a lot to learn from each other. Consider exchanging contact information with a few of your classmates so that, if you happen to miss a

> "Class is a lot better and more fun if you participate in it."
> —EMU Student

class, or if you think some conversation about how to approach a project would be useful to you, you have a way of connecting. Writing is a thoroughly social process. Setting up study sessions or writing days with your peers helps, especially if you are feeling unsure or tentative about a project or how to approach it.

Use available resources. It probably took some time for you to become aware of the range of resources and support services available to you in high school. College is similar. Eastern Michigan University provides numerous resources designed to support you in all aspects of college life. It may take some time to learn where these resources are located, and we have dedicated a section of this textbook to introducing you to some of the resources and support services most pertinent to your success in the First-Year Writing Program and in college, generally. If you are having a difficult time with any aspect of college life, know that you can turn to these resources and support services for prompt, professional guidance. Specifically in relation to the course, all instructors hold weekly office hours, and many will meet with students outside of their office hours if your schedules conflict. You will find more information about University resources in the opening section of your *EasyWriter* handbook.

Visit the University Writing Center (UWC). Do you ever sit, staring at a blank page or screen, willing your draft to write itself and wish you could just talk to someone about what you are working on? Well, that is what the University Writing Center is for. All writers, whether struggling or sailing through compositions with apparent ease, benefit from having constructive conversations about their work-in-progress. University Writing Center consultants are trained, thoughtful, and careful readers and listeners. They don't judge your work; they simply respond to your text as a reader would and provide supportive and appropriate recommendations. Writing Center sessions are most helpful when they happen well in advance of your due date. Don't wait until the date of your deadline to visit the UWC. Plan to work with a writing tutor at least a few days before your final project needs to be turned in to your instructor. For more information about the University Writing Center, visit **emich.edu/uwc**. The University Writing Center is located in 115 Halle Library and in 211 Pray-Harrold for your convenience.

Talk to your instructor. Because FYWP classes are small, instructors not only know your name but also care if you're in class, if you're feeling unsure about course material, and if you write something sophisticated and challenging. Instructors are your primary resource in first-year writing courses. So, take them up on their office hours, visit them, and

> "Make an effort to learn something that you do not already know. The lessons learned in this class will be valuable throughout your college time and your career."
>
> —EMU Student

ask questions. Getting individual feedback is one of the best ways to improve your writing. Ask your instructor specific, focused questions about your work, and make sure that you fully understand what is required for success on each course project.

Expectations for Your First-Year Writing Class

Discussion and Participation

Writing is a social process. Learning to write is underpinned by discussion and participation. By interacting with your classmates and your instructor this way, you are learning how to respond constructively to writing done by others and, as well, how to take feedback on your own ideas and your own writing. Each instructor will have different policies regarding discussion and participation, but you can expect that all sections of first-year writing will feature discussion and participation as a component of the in-class experience.

Feedback and Interaction

Writing improves through a process of sharing your work with other readers and taking their genuine responses into consideration. Throughout the semester, you will receive numerous comments, suggestions, and questions from your classmates, your instructor, and, if you visit the University Writing Center, writing consultants. All of their feedback is invaluable to you, and you will have decisions to make as a result: "Should I rearrange a section, moving it closer to the beginning? Should I cut this paragraph? How can I rewrite this sentence so it is clearer? Is my title both descriptive and attention-getting?" Revising according to responses from invested readers is tremendously important to effective communication practices.

Peer Review

Peer review goes hand in hand with feedback and interaction. It is a structured interaction, either in class or online, in which readers respond to a draft according to a series of specific questions or prompts. You will receive valuable feedback from the peer review process in first-year writing, and you will gain experience as a reviewer by reading and writing responses to your classmates. By reading another's project draft, you can also gain insights about the decisions you have made. Remember, good peer review feels like an engaged, energetic conversation about your ideas. And, like any conversation about ideas, there are elements that you will agree with and want to incorporate in your work, and elements that won't be as helpful for your project. So, filter. In the end, you're the author, and you have to feel comfortable with and have ownership of the final product.

STUDENT SUGGESTIONS FOR PEER REVIEW

- Talk with your classmate about your concerns as a writer.
- Listen carefully to your classmate express concerns about the draft.
- Ask permission before writing on a classmate's draft.
- Focus on more than editing a paper for grammar and mechanics; consider rhetorical concerns such as purpose and audience.
- Identify strengths of in addition to concerns regarding a project or project draft.

Reflection

Reflection names the conscious effort to look back at what has happened and to think about your approach, how you have done what you have done, and how you think and feel about it. In first-year writing classes, you will be asked frequently to reflect on your writing. The primary purpose of such reflections is to encourage conscious, deliberate decision-making in your compositions, particularly as they relate to audience, purpose, and context. Writing about your choices makes you more fully aware of the decisions you seem to make unconsciously. In the long-term, reflection helps you become a writer who notices subtleties and nuances—the small differences that make writing effective in a specific situation. Reflective writing practice helps you become a more flexible, adaptable, successful writer in other classes and outside of the classroom.

Celebration of Student Writing

The Celebration of Student Writing (CSW) is a program-wide showcase of research projects from WRTG 121. The CSW began at Eastern Michigan University in 2001, and similar celebrations are nowadays widespread across writing programs in the United States. Attendance and participation in the event is required for all sections and for all students, because it is a vital part of circulating your work publicly. Additionally, the event is linked with the portfolio assessment that caps both courses in the first-year writing sequence. The CSW is designed to reinforce presentational genres related to the semester-long research project in WRTG 121. The venue opens this work to a public audience for students while positioning them as contributing members of the academic community. The biannual event is open to the public as well as the university community.

33rd Semiannual	Thursday, November 30, 2017
34th Semiannual	Thursday, April 12, 2018
Time	3:30–5:30 p.m.
Location	EMU Student Center Grand Ballroom

Instructor Office Hours and Conferences

If you want to discuss your work or any questions you have about the class, or if you are uncertain about how to approach a project, visit your instructor during office hours. Each instructor holds regular office hours set aside to support your efforts and to guide you through the class. Your instructor's office hours and location are listed on the syllabus. If you cannot attend your instructor's regular office hours, talk with your instructor about setting an alternative meeting time on campus. Communication between you and your instructor is a key factor in assuring your learning, so do not hesitate to visit your instructor during office hours throughout the semester.

Additionally, many instructors require one-on-one or small group writing conferences during the semester. These conferences are highly beneficial, as they focus on your in-progress writing and reinforce key concepts and techniques addressed in class.

DISCUSSION QUESTIONS

1. Now that you have gained a sense of course and program expectations, what questions do you have? What seems interesting? What seems confusing?
2. How does this course structure resemble writing courses you have taken before? What seems new? What appears to be valued in this class?

UNDERSTANDING
RHETORIC

2nd Edition

a GRAPHIC GUIDE to WRITING

Elizabeth Losh
Jonathan Alexander
Kevin Cannon
Zander Cannon

 bedford/st.martin's
Macmillan Learning

BOSTON • NEW YORK

For Bedford/St. Martin's

Vice President, Editorial, Macmillan Learning Humanities: Edwin Hill
Editorial Director, English: Karen S. Henry
Senior Program Director: Leasa Burton
Program Manager: Molly Parke
Executive Editor: Carolyn Lengel
Senior Production Editor: Ryan Sullivan
Media Producer: Melissa Skepko-Masi
Senior Production Supervisor: Jennifer Wetzel
Executive Marketing Manager: Joy Fisher Williams
Indexer: Schroeder Indexing Services
Senior Photo Editor: Martha Friedman
Permissions Manager: Kalina K. Ingham
Senior Art Director: Anna Palchik
Cover Illustrators: Kevin Cannon, Zander Cannon
Printing and Binding: King Printing Co., Inc.

Manufactured in the United States of America.
2 1 0 9 8 7
f e d c b a

For information, write: Bedford/St. Martin's, 75 Arlington Street, Boston, MA 02116
  (617-399-4000)

ISBN 978-1-319-04213-4

Acknowledgments

Acknowledgments and copyrights appear on the same page as the text and art selections they cover; these acknowledgments and copyrights constitute an extension of the copyright page.

CONTENTS

PREFACE:
GETTING GRAPHIC

When we first began to work on *Understanding Rhetoric*, we expected other composition instructors to respond well to this comic-style text. We saw that comics were being assigned more frequently in writing courses, and we hoped our book would encourage students to engage deeply with core concepts of writing and rhetoric. By emphasizing multimodal approaches to composing, we wanted to engage student writers in thinking about their identities, contexts for their research, and effective writing processes. We also wanted to create a book that students would actually *want* to read—a book that could make rhetoric interesting and maybe even enjoyable.

> I REALLY LIKE THIS BOOK -- IT FILLED A NICHE FOR OUR STUDENT POPULATION THAT WAS OVERDUE TO BE FILLED.
>
> Sonja L. Andrus,
> *University of Cincinnati*

But we were still surprised by the level of enthusiasm that greeted *Understanding Rhetoric*, which shook up writing classrooms at more than 450 colleges and universities and which, instructors told us, got "nothing but positive responses from students." We were, and are, delighted that so many have responded so positively to the book. And we've benefited enormously from feedback from instructors and students who have been using it in their classrooms.

And so *Understanding Rhetoric*, Second Edition, was born. You'll find that this book still covers all the commonly taught topics in first-year composition, offering time-tested techniques for improving critical analysis, argumentation, and the development of research questions in college writing. As in the first edition, it contains practical tips for improving organization, identifying bias, evaluating sources, representing scholarly debates, and avoiding plagiarism. It includes new attention to collaborative writing, including peer review, and many new examples that students can use as models for analysis of their own. As always, it incorporates the latest research in composition, which focuses on the development of writers as well as writing.

> I LIKE THE FACT THAT IT'S ACCESSIBLE, BUT MORE THAN ANYTHING IT IS RHETORICALLY AWARE.
>
> Chris Gerben,
> *St. Edward's University*

Increasingly, composition instructors recognize that students need a range of literacy skills. The Web, video, blogging, YouTube, Tumblr, and social networking sites complement and challenge traditional text-based literacy practices, and students must consider the rhetorical requirements of writing for multimodal platforms—and must also see graphic design and visual evidence as basic tools for communication. After all, many of them may be doing most of their writing using such platforms. The graphic approach of *Understanding Rhetoric* supports instructors who want to teach with a book that—like the works their students interact with regularly—is both visually and textually rich.

> UNDERSTANDING RHETORIC PRACTICES WHAT WE PREACH ABOUT MULTIMODAL RHETORIC.
>
> Sarah F. McGinley,
> *Wright State University*

Understanding Rhetoric is arranged like a comic anthology, with nine issues dealing with individual rhetorical concepts. Each issue gives an in-depth look at the topic, reviews important points, suggests ways for students to put the concepts to use in their own work, and offers assignment ideas.

- Every issue begins with a chapter that takes a narrative approach to the rhetorical concept being discussed. The author characters interact with historical and fictional characters in comic panels that reward careful reading and that make complex ideas engaging and memorable.

- A "ReFrame" section after the chapter features student characters, Luis, Cindy, and Carol, grappling with the concepts and "walking through" a variety of texts.

- A "Drawing Conclusions" spread at the end of each issue suggests assignments that will allow students to try the concepts out for themselves.

Building on feedback from classroom users of *Understanding Rhetoric*, the second edition includes additional support for helping students get more out of peer review, for managing identities in context, and for doing research with library databases. It also includes more examples and quick advice for putting concepts into action. Look for the following new material:

- A new "Walk the Talk" feature in each chapter that walks students through analyzing an example text and reflecting on how they can use the chapter's concepts in their own reading, writing, and research

- Up-to-date advice on self-presentation in Chapter 3, "Writing Identities"

- A new Chapter 5, "Composing Together," which addresses the benefits of working together and practical strategies for making collaborations—including peer review—work smoothly

- An updated "ReFrame" section for Chapter 6, "Wrong Turns or Shortcuts?," featuring an expanded discussion of database research

In addition, the detailed instructor's manual will help both novice and experienced instructors plan a course around *Understanding Rhetoric*.

As you read through the text with your classes, ask students to pay attention not only to what the characters are saying, but to *how* information about writing and composing is conveyed both textually and visually. Our hands-on style emphasizes an active approach to writing, reading, and responding to all kinds of texts and emphasizes the dialogic nature of successful academic and public writing.

> THIS IS THE MOST SUCCESSFUL TEXT I HAVE EVER TAUGHT WITH IN TERMS OF STUDENT ENTHUSIASM.
>
> Jim Haendiges,
> *Dixie State University*

Ultimately, to enter into conversations (in good Burkean fashion) in different public spheres, writers should work through a series of interactions and discussions that allow them to craft insightful positions and compelling arguments. Our characters show how all writing is connected to identities. People write from particular positions, stances, and senses of self, and having a greater awareness of those positions—social, cultural, political, and historical—makes for more sophisticated and assured composing.

We hope you and your students enjoy *Understanding Rhetoric*. Most importantly, feel free as you teach with this book to talk back to us. Dare to disagree, either with us or other characters in the book. Get graphic with the text, and invite your students to draw and write within it. You might find yourself working with your students to make your own graphic guide to writing!

AUTHOR ACKNOWLEDGMENTS

We appreciate the contributions of the many, many individuals whose expertise and advice made this book possible.

Reviewers

We received invaluable feedback from a wonderful group of reviewers, whose suggestions helped us shape the direction of individual chapters and of the book as a whole during its entire development process:

Susan Achziger, Community College of Aurora; John Alberti, Northern Kentucky University; Ira Allen, American University of Beirut; Sonja Andrus, University of Cincinnati, Blue Ash College; Matt Barton, St. Cloud State University; David Beach, West Virginia University; Christiane Boehr, University of Cincinnati; Jeanne Bohannon, Kennesaw State University; Malkiel Choseed, Onondaga Community College; Jennifer deWinter, Worcester Polytechnic Institute; Summer Dickinson, Mid-Plains Community College; Misty Evans, Murray State University; Diana Fernandez, Barry University; Chris Gerben, St. Edward's University; Jim Haendiges, Dixie State University; Sabrina Hardy, Liberty University; Wendy Hayden, Hunter College of the City University of New York; Chris Cormier Hayes, Simmons College; Marcy Isabella, Stockton University; William Lalicker, West Chester University; Bonnie Markowski, University of Scranton; Christine Masters, Purdue University; Jessica Matthews, George Mason University; Sarah McGinley, Wright State University; Erin McLaughlin, University of Notre Dame; Jessica Miller, Eastern Michigan University; Elizabeth Monske, Northern Michigan University; Jill Morris, Frostburg State University; Alice Myatt, University of Mississippi; Jessica Nastal-Dema, Georgia Southern University; Danielle Nielsen, Murray State University; Kate Pantelides, Eastern Michigan University;

Michael Pemberton, Georgia Southern University; Melody Pugh, United States Air Force Academy; Rachael Ryerson, Ohio University; Molly Scanlon, Nova Southeastern University; Marc Scott, Shawnee State University; Kassia Shaw, Waubonsee Community College; Aleksandra Swatek, Purdue University; Benjamin Syn, University of Colorado, Colorado Springs; Heidi Thoenen, University of Akron; Stephanie Vie, University of Central Florida; Shevaun Watson, University of Wisconsin–Eau Claire; Kristen Weinzapfel, North Central Texas College; Chantay White-Williams, Southwestern Illinois College; Jennifer Williams, Chandler-Gilbert Community College; Julie Winslett, University of North Georgia; and Melody Wise, Glenville State College.

Contributors
We would like to acknowledge some of the people whose ideas and suggestions helped in the creation of this book: Norah Ashe, University of Southern California; Greg Benford, University of California, Irvine; Vinayak Chaturvedi, University of California, Irvine; Michael Clark, University of California, Irvine; James Paul Gee, Arizona State University; Brook Haley, University of California, Irvine; Michael Householder, Southern Methodist University; Julia Lupton, University of California, Irvine; Steven Mailloux, Loyola Marymount University; Lynn Malley, University of California, Irvine; Michele Mason, University of Maryland; Robert Moeller, University of California, Irvine; Erika Nanes, University of Southern California; Miriam Posner, University of California, Los Angeles; Terri Senft, New York University; Ellen Strenski; Brook Thomas, University of California, Irvine; Phil Troutman, George Washington University; and Ann Van Sant, University of California, Irvine.

Many thanks to Marissa Osato, a graduate of the University of California, Irvine, for allowing us to adapt content from her essay on Japanese Americans in internment camps during World War II; Uzair

Mohammad, a graduate of the University of California, San Diego, for allowing us to adapt content from his LinkedIn page; and Mel Chua for making her graphic research paper "What Is Engineering?" available with a Creative Commons license.

We are very grateful to Tom Gammill for his illustrations in Chapter 6.

Special thanks are in order to Keith McCleary and Jasmine Lee for their work on the instructor's manual, which was radically redeveloped for this edition.

For contributions to our initial thinking on instructional materials for *Understanding Rhetoric*, our gratitude goes to Henry Jenkins, Emily Roxworthy, Molly Scanlon, Cynthia Selfe, and Wayne Yang.

We are grateful to Thomas LeBien of Hill & Wang and to Jessica Marshall for helpful initial feedback on this project.

Finally, we would like to thank Zander Cannon and Kevin Cannon, our coauthors, for turning our manuscript into a real comic book. They contributed not just illustrations, but also many great ideas for conveying concepts visually—and a lot of good jokes.

Bedford/St. Martin's
Everyone on the team at Bedford/St. Martin's was critical for bringing this second edition to fruition. Constructive and creative feedback—from Leasa Burton, Carolyn Lengel, Molly Parke, and others—over the course of many lively conversations was central to our writing process. We are grateful to Anna Palchik for her art direction; to our project editor, Ryan Sullivan; and to our marketing manager, Joy Fisher Williams.

Elizabeth Losh, *The College of William and Mary*
Jonathan Alexander, *University of California, Irvine*

We would like to thank everyone at Bedford/St. Martin's for their support, encouragement, and enthusiasm over the course of making this book. In particular we'd like to thank Leasa Burton, Carolyn Lengel, and Molly Parke for their vision and guidance in seeing this book through from an idea to a finished project, and we'd like to thank Anna Palchik, Deb Baker, and Ryan Sullivan for their support on the art and technical end.

Big thanks also go out to our coauthors, Liz and Jonathan, for being nimble with their script and adaptable to the peculiarities of making a comic book, and to all the additional challenges of making that comic book informative and educational. Finally, we appreciate the support of Thomas LeBien, who recommended us as artists for *Understanding Rhetoric* in the first place.

Also, Zander would like to thank his wife, Julie, and their son, Jin, for their support and for making their home a happy place to return to at the end of the day.

Kevin Cannon
Zander Cannon

SPACES FOR WRITING

In this issue...

DISCOVERING CONTEXTS FOR WRITING

THIS BOOK -- IN ITS CONTENT, ITS FORMAT, AND ITS LAYOUT -- PLAYS WITH THE IDEA THAT PEOPLE WRITE IN MANY DIFFERENT PLACES AND SPACES.

New Release!

SELF-HELP ~~REFERENCE~~ ??

UNDERSTANDING RHETORIC
2nd Edition
a GRAPHIC GUIDE to WRITING
LOSH · ALEXANDER · CANNON · CANNON

NOT NECESSARILY IN THIS KIND OF SPACE --

-- THOUGH HUMANS HAVE SENT MESSAGES TO THE STARS --

-- BUT IN DIFFERENT SOCIAL SPACES THAT AFFECT HOW WE COMMUNICATE, WHAT IS SAID, WHAT IS NOT SAID...

...AND HOW OUR MESSAGES ARE RECEIVED, UNDERSTOOD, AND ACTED UPON.

LIZ

JONATHAN

OFTEN, WHEN PEOPLE TALK ABOUT BEGINNING A WRITING PROJECT, THIS IS WHAT THEY THINK ABOUT:

THE BLANK PAGE.

IT'S A WAY TO VISUALIZE ISOLATION, SOLITUDE, AND LONELINESS; STRUGGLING WITH ONE'S SOUL IN A PRIVATE ROOM; AGONIZING OVER WORD AFTER WORD; DILIGENTLY WAITING FOR **INSPIRATION!**

OR THEY ARE AWASH IN IDEAS, INSIGHTS, AND OBSERVATIONS THAT CROWD OUT THEIR ABILITY TO THINK CLEARLY AND COMMUNICATE CONCISELY.

THERE'S SO MUCH TO SAY -- HOW DO YOU KNOW WHAT'S WORTH SAYING? AND WHEN TO SAY IT? AND HOW?

TO HELP YOU EXAMINE THE ELEMENTS OF THE WRITING SITUATION, MAKE SENSE OF THEM...

...TAKE ADVANTAGE OF THE OPPORTUNITIES THAT THEY PRESENT, AND AVOID THE PITFALLS...

...WE ARE USING BOTH IMAGES AND TEXT TO CONVEY OUR ADVICE.

...WE ARE USING BOTH IMAGES AND TEXT TO CONVEY OUR ADVICE.

WHAT WE'RE DOING IN THIS BOOK ISN'T ACTUALLY A NEW APPROACH.

IN FACT, NINETEENTH-CENTURY BOOKS ON RHETORIC OFTEN INCORPORATED ILLUSTRATIONS AND DIAGRAMS TO HELP THEIR READERS BECOME BETTER SPEAKERS AND WRITERS.

Gilbert Austin
CHIRONOMIA SPHERE

ORATORY

We are simply taking this approach one step further, by bringing ourselves into the illustrations.

JONATHAN AND I ARE HERE TO SERVE AS YOUR GUIDES--

-- TO LEAD YOU THROUGH THE PROCESS OF BECOMING A MORE EFFECTIVE COMMUNICATOR.

GOING BOLDLY THROUGH WRITING PROCESSES

11

Introduction

...AND THAT MAY BE ONE OF THE MOST IMPORTANT LESSONS ABOUT LEARNING TO WRITE AND COMMUNICATE EFFECTIVELY.

WHEN WE WERE WORKING ON THIS COMIC, FOR INSTANCE, WE KNEW THAT WE WOULD HAVE TO REVISE WHAT WE WROTE BASED ON WHAT THE ILLUSTRATORS DREW.

SOMETIMES KEVIN AND ZANDER DREW EXACTLY WHAT WE HAD IN MIND.

AND OTHER TIMES, THEY HAD **BETTER** IDEAS.

FAINT!

UNCORRECTED PROOF

IF WE HADN'T ALL BEEN WILLING TO WORK WITH OTHERS' SUGGESTIONS, WE WOULD HAVE HAD A VERY LIMITED AND UNSATISFACTORY BOOK!

"Perfect manuscript"

SO WORKING COLLABORATIVELY FROM THE BEGINNING WAS A CRUCIAL COMPONENT OF OUR COMPOSING PROCESS.

AND NOW, BECAUSE WE ARE USING BOTH IMAGES AND WORDS TO CONVEY OUR ADVICE, WE WANT TO SAY SOMETHING ABOUT VISUAL LITERACY.

EXPLORING VISUAL LITERACY

CONSIDER THIS: WHEN A PHOTOGRAPH APPEARS IN THE PAGES OF A GRAPHIC NOVEL, WE KNOW THAT IT HAS A SPECIAL SIGNIFICANCE.

IT LOOKS DIFFERENT FROM THE OTHER PICTURES ON THE PAGE.

IT SEEMS TO DEPICT MORE ACCURATELY THE WAY THAT SOMEONE OR SOMETHING LOOKS IN REAL LIFE.

SO, AT THIS MOMENT, A PERSON WHO OPENS TO THESE PAGES IN THIS BOOK CAN COMPARE THE APPEARANCE OF THE CARTOON ME TO THE ME OF THE PHOTOGRAPH.

IT DOESN'T TAKE CAREFUL VIEWING TO SEE THAT THE ARTISTS HAVE SIMPLIFIED AND ABSTRACTED THE WAY JONATHAN LOOKS.

IN COMPARISON, THE PHOTOGRAPH PROBABLY SEEMS MUCH CLOSER TO SHOWING THE "REAL TRUTH."

WE USUALLY ASSOCIATE HAND-DRAWN IMAGES WITH WORKS OF THE IMAGINATION...

...WHILE PHOTOGRAPHS CREATED BY A MACHINE LIKE A CAMERA ARE SUPPOSED TO GIVE US THE REAL STORY, THE FACTS.

HOWEVER, WE KNOW THAT, JUST LIKE A DRAWING, A PHOTOGRAPH IS REALLY ONLY A REPRESENTATION.

DONK DONK

AFTER ALL, I CAN'T REACH IN AND ACTUALLY TOUCH THIS DESK.

MAYBE I CAN.

BUT THE READER CAN'T. IT'S A STATIC IMAGE THAT EXISTS ONLY IN TWO DIMENSIONS ON THE PAGE.

A PHOTOGRAPH IS NOT JUST A "PICTURE OF REALITY."

THERE ARE ACTUALLY MANY CONCEPTUAL DIMENSIONS TO ANY IMAGE.

THIS SECTION OF OUR BOOK IS ABOUT WHAT IMAGES MEAN AS WELL AS SHOW.

I WONDER WHAT THOSE STUDENTS ARE LAUGHING ABOUT?.

JUST ADDING WORDS CAN CHANGE THE ENTIRE MEANING OF AN IMAGE.

AND THE FRAMING OF THE CONTENT MATTERS, TOO.

FOR EXAMPLE, WHEN AN IMAGE IS CROPPED IN A CERTAIN WAY, OR WHEN AN ILLUSTRATION SHOWS A DETAIL INSTEAD OF ZOOMING OUT TO SHOW A BIGGER PICTURE, THE ENTIRE MEANING OF THE IMAGE CAN CHANGE.

IN THIS VERSION, WE DON'T SEE A PROFESSIONAL SETTING.

THE IMAGE SENDS A VERY DIFFERENT MESSAGE WITHOUT THE OFFICIAL AND IMPOSING BACK-DROP OF AN OFFICE.

THEN, IF WE SEE MORE INFORMATION IN THE FRAME, THE MEANING CHANGES YET AGAIN.

THIS VERSION OF THE IMAGE IS MUCH MORE PLAYFUL AND SUBVERSIVE.

(Photos) Mack McCoy

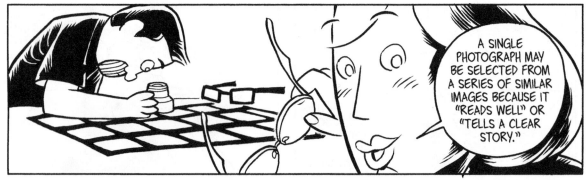

A SINGLE PHOTOGRAPH MAY BE SELECTED FROM A SERIES OF SIMILAR IMAGES BECAUSE IT "READS WELL" OR "TELLS A CLEAR STORY."

LEARNING TO READ THE DIFFERENT ELEMENTS OF A VISUAL TEXT IS PART OF WHAT WE CALL VISUAL LITERACY.

VISUAL LITERACY IS VERY IMPORTANT IN UNDERSTANDING THE MESSAGES THAT ARE CONVEYED BY PHOTOGRAPHY AND ILLUSTRATION...

...AND BY PAINTING, GRAPHIC DESIGN, SCULPTURE, ARCHITECTURE, VIDEO -- ANY MEDIA THAT WE ENGAGE WITH OUR EYES.

WHEN WE SEE IMAGES IN A WORK OF ART OR IN A FILM, WE PAY ATTENTION TO THE CRAFT OF INTENTIONAL COMPOSITION.

WE MAY NEED TO LOOK VERY CLOSELY AND INVEST TIME TO UNDERSTAND HOW THE VISUAL ELEMENTS TELL A STORY.

OUR CULTURE HAS TAUGHT US THAT DEPICTING CLOSENESS OR DISTANCE IN AN IMAGE MIGHT SUGGEST SOMETHING ABOUT THE INTIMACY BETWEEN THE PEOPLE SHOWN.

BECAUSE VISUAL LITERACY IS SUCH AN IMPORTANT PART OF OUR CULTURE, WE HAVE CHOSEN TO

CREATE THIS BOOK IN THE FORM! OF! A! COMIC!

PART OF OUR DECISION TO WRITE A GRAPHIC BOOK HAS TO DO WITH THE PORTABILITY OF OUR MESSAGE.

INCREASINGLY, A VARIETY OF ARGUMENTS ARE BEING MADE AND SHARED THROUGH VISUALLY RICH MEDIA SUCH AS THE WEB.

...BUT MORE ON THAT IN LATER CHAPTERS.

IDEAS ABOUT THE MEANING OF VISUAL REPRESENTATIONS AND HOW THEY HELP US TELL STORIES HAVE A LONG HISTORY IN OUR CULTURE. THEY DIDN'T JUST EMERGE WITH THE INVENTION OF THE COMIC!

INDEED.

THE RENAISSANCE WRITER LEON BATTISTA ALBERTI HAD STRONG IDEAS ABOUT HOW IMAGES TOLD A STORY.

DON'T USE GOLD PAINT!

YOU THINK THE GOLD MAKES YOUR PAINTING LOOK RARE AND PRECIOUS, BUT IT JUST SHOWS THAT YOU ARE AN AMATEUR WHO CAN ONLY RELY ON CHEAP TRICKS.

ARTISTS ASSOCIATED WITH **DE STIJL**, A TWENTIETH-CENTURY DUTCH SCHOOL OF ART, BECAME FAMOUS FOR THEIR USE OF PRIMARY COLORS AND SIMPLE GEOMETRY.

PIET MONDRIAN

THEO VAN DOESBURG

THEY ALSO ENGAGED IN FIERCE DEBATES.

VERTICAL AND HORIZONTAL LINES HAVE HARMONY AND ORDER!

DIAGONAL LINES SHOULD BE FORBIDDEN! FORWARD-LOOKING ARTISTS STICK TO VERTICAL AND HORIZONTAL LINES!

DIAGONAL LINES REPRESENT THE FUTURE!

THEY HAVE SO MUCH MORE ENERGY THAN YOUR STAID VERTICAL AND HORIZONTAL LINES.

%.&?!

&?

ACTUALLY, THE THINGS THAT THOSE ARTISTS ARGUED ABOUT STILL MATTER AS WE TRY TO UNDERSTAND THE VISUAL LANGUAGES THAT WE ARE EXPOSED TO EVERY DAY.

THIS IS THE LOGO FOR THE HUMAN RIGHTS CAMPAIGN, A GROUP THAT WORKS FOR EQUALITY FOR LGBTQ AMERICANS.

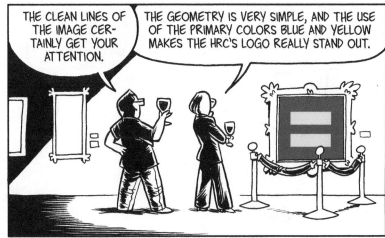

THE CLEAN LINES OF THE IMAGE CERTAINLY GET YOUR ATTENTION.

THE GEOMETRY IS VERY SIMPLE, AND THE USE OF THE PRIMARY COLORS BLUE AND YELLOW MAKES THE HRC'S LOGO REALLY STAND OUT.

IT USES **NEGATIVE SPACE** TO DRAW THE VIEWER'S EYES TO THE CHANNEL BETWEEN THE TWO RECTANGLES, WHICH CONNECTS THE SPACES ON EITHER SIDE.

THE IMAGE ALSO USES **SYMMETRY**.

TOP AND BOTTOM AND RIGHT AND LEFT MIRROR EACH OTHER.

IF WE READ THE IMAGE CAREFULLY, WE SEE THAT THE HUMAN RIGHTS CAMPAIGN LOGO GETS OUR ATTENTION, BUT IT ISN'T INTENDED TO SHOCK US.

IT IS AN IMAGE OF HARMONY AND BALANCE.

CRITICS MIGHT EVEN SAY THAT IT IS AN IMAGE ABOUT NOT STANDING UP OR STICKING OUT.

(Photo) Mack McCoy

IF THE WHOLE COMIC BOOK WERE MADE OF PHOTOGRAPHS, WHAT WOULD BE LEFT FOR US TO DRAW?

WELL, SOMEONE WOULD STILL HAVE TO THINK ABOUT WHAT TO SHOW AND FIGURE OUT THE BEST WAY TO SHOW IT.

THAT'S TRUE.

THE BOOK AS A WHOLE WOULD STILL HAVE TO MAKE A GOOD VISUAL ARGUMENT.

CRUMPLE

SPEAKING OF VISUAL ARGUMENTS, WHY DO YOU ALWAYS DRAW SO MANY DIAGONAL LINES?

UH...

...I DON'T THINK THAT'S THE KIND OF ARGUMENT THEY MEAN.

BUT WHY DO YOU USE SO MANY DIAGONAL LINES?

REFRAME with Luis & Cindy

Why rhetoric? Why a COMIC BOOK?

Odio cuando mi madre insiste en hablar en vietnamita frente a la gente.

[I HATE IT WHEN MY MOTHER INSISTS ON SPEAKING IN VIETNAMESE IN FRONT OF PEOPLE.]

MY DAUGHTER IS VERY GOOD WITH LANGUAGES.

I CAN SEE THAT.

Yo no estaba coqueteando contigo. Yo sólo estaba siendo amable.

[I WASN'T FLIRTING WITH YOU. I WAS JUST BEING FRIENDLY.]

WHOOPS!

I NEVER THOUGHT I'D COME TO COLLEGE AND MY FIRST TEXT-BOOK WOULD BE A **COMIC BOOK!**

I KNOW WHAT YOU MEAN.

I **LIKE** COMICS, BUT I DON'T THINK OF THEM AS **TEXTBOOKS.**

C'MON, IT'S ONLY THE FIRST DAY OF CLASS.

KEEP AN **OPEN MIND!**

MY MOM'S READING IT TOO!

SHE'S TAKING NIGHT CLASSES, AND HER TEACHER IS USING THE SAME BOOK!

I NEVER THOUGHT I'D BE GOING BACK TO SCHOOL SO LATE, BUT AT LEAST MY DAUGHTER AND I CAN STUDY TOGETHER!

BUT MY CLASS IS ACTUALLY **HARDER** THAN HERS.

WE'RE ALSO **CREATING** GRAPHIC NOVELS THAT TELL THE STORIES OF OUR OWN LIVES.

THEY'RE CALLED **MEMOIRS**, MOTHER.

GRAPHIC MEMOIRS.

MY SPANISH MAY NOT BE GREAT, BUT MY ENGLISH IS FINE.

I HOPE YOU DON'T TALK THIS WAY TO **YOUR** MOTHER.

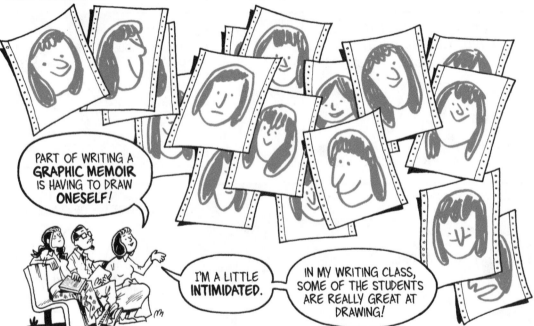
PART OF WRITING A **GRAPHIC MEMOIR** IS HAVING TO DRAW **ONESELF!**

I'M A LITTLE **INTIMIDATED**.

IN MY WRITING CLASS, SOME OF THE STUDENTS ARE REALLY GREAT AT DRAWING!

BUT THERE ARE A LOT OF THINGS THAT THOSE STUDENTS **DON'T** KNOW HOW TO DO.

LIKE **PAY ATTENTION**.

SOME OF THEM HAVE MANNERS THAT ARE ALMOST AS BAD AS HERS.

COME ON, MOM. I'M SURE THAT THE OTHER STUDENTS AREN'T REALLY THAT BAD.

YOU SHOULD TRY TO MAKE FRIENDS.

I DON'T WANT TO TALK ABOUT OUR PERSONAL BUSINESS.

YOU SHOULDN'T BE EMBARRASSED, MOM.

AND BEING A GOOD ARTIST DOESN'T REALLY MATTER AS MUCH AS YOU THINK IT DOES.

IT SOUNDS LIKE THE PROJECT IS ABOUT TELLING A COMPELLING STORY AND MAKING AN INTERESTING VISUAL ARGUMENT.

LIKE IN MY LAB REPORT HERE, I HAVE TO USE THESE CHARTS AND GRAPHS TO CONVINCE THE TEACHER THAT I'VE DONE THE EXPERIMENT CORRECTLY.

CHARTS AND GRAPHS ARE ONE THING. BUT WHAT DO I DO WITH THIS PAGE SHOWING MY TIME IN THE REFUGEE CAMP ENGLISH CLASS?

...IT FEELS TOO **DENSE** OR SOMETHING.

Hello.

ACTUALLY, IT'S REALLY INTERESTING TO SEE HOW MUCH INFORMATION YOU PACK INTO THE PAGE.

BUT WHAT IF YOU REALLY DEVELOPED THE CHARACTER OF YOUR TEACHER?

YOU COULD BREAK UP THIS FRAME INTO INDIVIDUAL FRAMES, AND WE WOULD KNOW THAT YOU WERE SHOWING DIFFERENT EPISODES IN TIME.

COMING UP IN THE NEXT EXCITING EPISODE OF **REFRAME**

"What does ARISTOTLE have to do with ME?"

[pg 57]

"RHETORICAL SITUATIONS"

WHAT DO WE HAVE HERE? A NAME AND EMAIL ADDRESS...

...AND "PROUDLY DRAWN BY AN ENGINEER ON ENGINEERING PAPER"!

1 WHO WROTE THIS?

SEE WHAT YOU CAN LEARN OR INFER ABOUT THE WRITER.

"AT 2 A.M." MIGHT MEAN MEL CHUA IS A **STUDENT**!

°/5

WHAT IS

ENGINEERING?

A GRAPHIC ESSAY OF TECH AND PHILOSOPHY

PROUDLY DRAWN

BY AN ENGINEER

ON ENGINEERING PAPER

AT 2AM

MEL CHUA
<MEL@MELCHUA.COM>
CC-BY-SA 2011

THIS UNUSUAL COVER PAGE PROVIDES A LOT OF INFORMATION ABOUT THE RHETORICAL SITUATION.

THIS WRITER IS PLAYING WITH READERS' EXPECTATIONS, TRYING OUT ROLES, AND APPEALING TO A VARIETY OF AUDIENCES.

WHAT'S **YOUR** TAKE?

DRAWING CONCLUSIONS

The following assignments ask you to try out the
concepts discussed in this Introduction.

1 Start a journal in which you make a list
of the genres and visual metaphors you
see throughout *Understanding Rhetoric*
(like the science-fiction elements in the
Introduction). After each chapter, write
a response discussing how visual elements
affect your interpretation of the book.

Keep the journal all semester, and at the end
of the course write a final reflection about
how your discussion of visuals changed from
the beginning to the end of the course.

genres &
visual
metaphors

2 Try to read just the text—
not the images—on page 2
of the Introduction.

Write or talk with your
classmates about what you think
this text means. Then examine
the illustrations on page 2.

What do the visuals seem to
say on their own? How do they
change the meaning of the text?

3

In the ReFrame for this chapter, Carol is working on her graphic memoir. Using both words and images, make a draft of what your own graphic memoir might look like.

What would you choose to emphasize? How would you make your central ideas and themes clear?

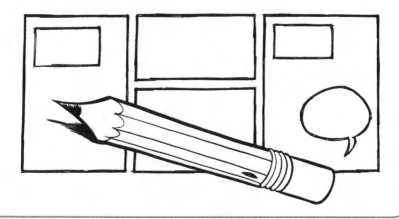

4

Comic artists often arrange panels to suggest different perceptions of time. Browse graphic novels or other comics to find creative depictions of the experience of passing time. Then create a storyboard for a short comic about an event that seemed to you to occur much more slowly or more quickly than you know it actually did.

Present your storyboard to others in your class and get feedback on how well your method works.

IS THAT A RHETORICAL QUESTION?!!

HMF.

SOME PEOPLE CALL A QUESTION **"RHETORICAL"** BECAUSE NO ANSWER IS ACTUALLY EXPECTED.

DO I LOOK **STUPID** TO YOU?

ACCORDING TO THEM, RHETORIC AND RHETORICAL ARE ALL ABOUT **SHUTTING DOWN** CONVERSATION AND DEBATE!

BUT I--

ACTUALLY, THE ANCIENTS DEVELOPED THE CONCEPT OF **RHETORIC** TO **FACILITATE** DISCUSSION.

THEY THOUGHT THAT RHETORIC PROVIDED A SET OF SKILLS THAT HELPED PEOPLE FOREGROUND IDEAS --

-- DISCUSS AND DEBATE THEIR THOUGHTS WITH OTHERS --

-- AND POTENTIALLY REACH COMMON GOALS OR MAKE DIFFICULT DECISIONS.

IN THE ORIGINAL GREEK, THE WORD **RHETORIC** COMES FROM THE VERB **EIRO**, "TO SAY."

memories feelings logic

BUT RHETORIC IS MUCH MORE THAN JUST **TALK**.

IT'S A WAY OF **THINKING** ABOUT HOW WE TALK...

values

insights

beliefs

...THAT TAKES INTO CONSIDERATION THE ENTIRE SITUATION IN WHICH THAT TALK TAKES PLACE.

RHETORIC IS ABOUT THE **SPACES** IN WHICH WE WRITE, CONVERSE, DEBATE, AND SHARE **IDEAS**.

MANY COMMONLY HELD NEGATIVE IDEAS ABOUT RHETORIC CAN BE TRACED TO THE ANCIENT GREEK PHILOSOPHER **PLATO.**

HE BELIEVED THAT TEACHERS LIKE US WHO TAUGHT RHETORIC WERE INSTRUCTING THEIR STUDENTS TO DECEIVE OTHERS RATHER THAN TO BETTER THEMSELVES.

IF SERIOUS DISCUSSION IS LIKE GYMNASTICS, THEN RHETORIC IS LIKE **COSMETICS.**

RHETORIC IS INTENDED ONLY TO HIDE FLAWS, NOT ENCOURAGE SELF-IMPROVEMENT.

PLATO (427–347 BCE)
ANCIENT GREEK PHILOSOPHER, STUDENT OF SOCRATES, AND FOUNDER OF THE ATHENIAN ACADEMY, AN IMPORTANT EARLY SCHOOL OF THOUGHT.

AS FAR AS PLATO WAS CONCERNED, RHETORIC WAS AN EMPTY, UNWHOLESOME DISTRACTION THAT TOOK ATTENTION AWAY FROM IMPORTANT PHILOSOPHICAL AND CIVIC MATTERS.

INDULGING THE POPULATION'S APPETITE FOR RHETORIC IS AS BAD AS SELLING **PASTRIES** INSTEAD OF DISPENSING **MEDICINE.**

PLATO ALSO THOUGHT THAT VIVID MEDIA EXPERIENCES, SUCH AS ANCIENT GREEK TRAGEDIES THAT SHOWED EXPLICIT SEX AND VIOLENCE, WOULD HAVE A BAD INFLUENCE ON YOUNG PEOPLE.

ALL POETS AND PLAYWRIGHTS SHOULD BE **BANISHED!**

PLATO FELT THAT THE YOUNG SHOULD BE PROTECTED FROM AMBIGUOUS MORAL MESSAGES.

PRETENDING TO BE CRIMINALS CAUSES CHILDREN TO GROW UP TO BE CRIMINALS IN REAL LIFE. EVERYONE KNOWS THAT.

PLATO WASN'T JUST WORRIED ABOUT CHILDREN. HE BELIEVED THAT THE INVENTION OF WRITING IN THE ANCIENT WORLD ALLOWED ADULTS TO LIE ABOUT THE TRUTH, PRETEND TO BE SOMEONE THEY WERE NOT, OR FORGET THE PAST AND TRADITION.

JUST AS PEOPLE WORRY TODAY ABOUT MANY OF THE EFFECTS OF TECHNOLOGY ON WRITING, PLATO WORRIED ABOUT THE EFFECT OF WRITING ON OUR ABILITY TO SPEAK THE TRUTH.

eHarmonium

Please Describe Yourself:
(Be ACCURATE!)
NAME: STUDICUS MAXIMUS
HAIR: FLOWING
HYGIENE: IMPECCABLE
DENTAL ISSUES: NONE
OCCUPATION: MODEL

THINGS WERE SURE A LOT BETTER BEFORE WE HAD **WRITING!**

PLATO'S STUDENT **ARISTOTLE** HAD A VERY DIFFERENT VIEW ABOUT WRITING AND RHETORIC.

PLATO   ARISTOTLE

ARISTOTLE WAS A PROPONENT OF THE USE OF RHETORIC TO PUT ACROSS A BROAD RANGE OF IDEAS.

ARISTOTLE (384–322 BCE)
ANCIENT GREEK PHILOSOPHER (AND STUDENT OF PLATO) WHOSE THINKING CONTRIBUTED MUCH TO THE DEVELOPMENT OF WESTERN EMPIRICAL AND SCIENTIFIC THOUGHT.

ARISTOTLE THOUGHT THAT PLAYS COULD SERVE AN **EDUCATIONAL** PURPOSE BY ENCOURAGING GREEK CITIZENS TO DEVELOP THEIR CAPACITIES FOR PITY AND FEAR.

BY SEEING THE CONSEQUENCES OF SEXUAL AND VIOLENT CRIMES THAT WERE COMMITTED BY ACTORS ON STAGE, SPECTATORS COULD LEARN **NOT** TO IMITATE **BAD ACTIONS.**

IN *THE ART OF RHETORIC,*

ETHOS

IS THE CREDIBILITY THAT A SPEAKER OR WRITER BRINGS TO THE SUBJECT THAT HE OR SHE IS COMMUNICATING ABOUT.

WE TRUST CERTAIN KINDS OF PEOPLE MORE THAN OTHERS -- BECAUSE THEY HAVE EXPERTISE, OR BECAUSE THEY ARE WELL INFORMED ABOUT THE SUBJECT AT HAND.

PATHOS

IS THE USE OF EMOTION IN DEBATE OR ARGUMENT.

APPEALS TO PATHOS SURROUND US, PARTICULARLY IN VISUAL ARGUMENTS SUCH AS ADVERTISEMENTS AND MANY ONLINE VIDEOS.

LOGOS

IS THE APPEAL TO REASON, TO THE FORCEFULNESS OF A WELL-THOUGHT-OUT AND WELL-STRUCTURED POSITION.

SOME ARGUMENTS MAKE MORE **LOGICAL** SENSE THAN OTHERS, AND MANY CONSIDER LOGOS TO BE CRITICAL IN THE DEVELOPMENT AND DISSEMINATION OF IDEAS AND VALUES.

LEARNING TO RECOGNIZE THESE CONCEPTS WILL HELP YOU UNDERSTAND OTHER PEOPLE'S ARGUMENTS.

YOU'LL ALSO STRENGTHEN YOUR OWN POSITION AND THE WAY OTHERS SEE YOU.

ETHOS PATHOS LOGOS

ETHOS PATHOS LOGOS

FOR EXAMPLE, AN ONLINE PROFILE IS A RHETORICAL SPACE IN WHICH ETHOS, PATHOS, AND LOGOS ARE VERY IMPORTANT.

ONLINE PROFILES ALLOW USERS TO CREATE RICH, ENGAGING, AND SOMETIMES SATIRIC SELF-PORTRAITS.

Jonathan likes:

Douglass   Aristotle   Jet-Skis

Lincoln   Funny Hats   The US Constitution

Asian Food   Monkeys!

ocial Network

Jonathan is thinking about getting a new computer.

Plato: Pff! It would just be the shadow of the CONCEPT of a computer, anyway.

Aristotle: Ooh, but the new X432g's are so AWESOME!
👎 1 DISLIKE

Jonathan wonders if he should eat some breakfast.

Aristotle: 1) Consider the pros and cons, 2) ask an expert, and 3) do it if you're hungry.

THE MIX OF PICTURES, VIDEO, AND TEXT CAN ESTABLISH -- OR **DESTROY** -- YOUR CREDIBILITY, OR **ETHOS**.

FOR INSTANCE, IF JONATHAN, AS A PROFESSOR OF ENGLISH, HAS A PROFILE RIDDLED WITH TYPOS AND IMAGES OF HIM GETTING DRUNK WITH HIS STUDENTS...

Social Network

Jonathan: Oh HAI I am Drunk with studentz !!!1!!

HIS CRED-IBILITY MIGHT **RISE** WITH SOME, BUT FALL WITH MOST OTHERS.

IMAGES AND WORDS CAN ALSO CONTRIBUTE TO THE PATHOS OF A PAGE...

ONE DAY:

Liz: is fine, keeping busy with work.

BUT THE NEXT:

Liz: is mourning the loss of a beloved cat.

"SNOOKUMS"
1999   2012

CERTAINLY, **PATHOS** IS BEING USED HERE TO PROMOTE SYMPATHY FOR LIZ...

...AND PERHAPS GENERATE A FEW KIND WORDS FOR HER **PAGE**.

WE GENERALLY DON'T THINK OF SOCIAL NETWORK PROFILES AS MAKING "LOGICAL ARGUMENTS," BUT IN A WAY, THEY **ARE** MAKING ARGUMENTS --

-- ARGUMENTS ABOUT WHO WE ARE, WHAT WE ARE INTERESTED IN, AND WHY SOMEONE MIGHT WANT TO "FRIEND" US.

@JONATHAN: Are you trying to seem cool by having a social network homepage?

BUT RHETORIC ISN'T JUST ABOUT **SPACE**. IT IS ALSO ABOUT **TIME**.

BENDING TIME through KAIROS

ALL OF US HAVE HAD EXPERIENCES THAT WERE EMBARRASSING, INSULTING, HUMILIATING, OR DEMORALIZING.

OFTEN WE WISH THAT WE COULD HAVE TRAVELED BACK IN TIME TO SAY JUST THE RIGHT THING AT THAT PARTICULAR MOMENT.

WE MAY COME UP WITH THE PERFECT THING TO HAVE SAID MUCH LATER, BUT IT IS ALREADY TOO LATE.

TONGUE TIED

LUMP IN THROAT

SHORT OF BREATH

RACING HEART

BUTTERFLIES IN STOMACH

RUBBER KNEES

today: AUDITIONS 5-9 pm

I-I KNOW YOU ARE, BUT WHAT AM I...?

DEBATES ABOUT DIFFICULT ISSUES ARE OFTEN TIME-SENSITIVE.

...VOTING TO REDUCE SPENDING ON UNIVERSITIES...

REELECT ME

BUT...

TUITION BILL

OFTEN, THERE IS A NARROW WINDOW WITHIN WHICH ONE CAN SPEAK OUT TO AFFECT AN ISSUE.

IN A LEGAL PROCEEDING, PARTICIPANTS ARE EXPECTED TO SPEAK ONLY AT CERTAIN TIMES.

...right to peaceably assemble...

...AND PRAISE OR BLAME FOR PEOPLE IN THE PUBLIC EYE MAY SWAY OPINIONS AT CRUCIAL MOMENTS.

MY CONGRESSM STANDS UP FOR STUDENTS DOES YOURS?

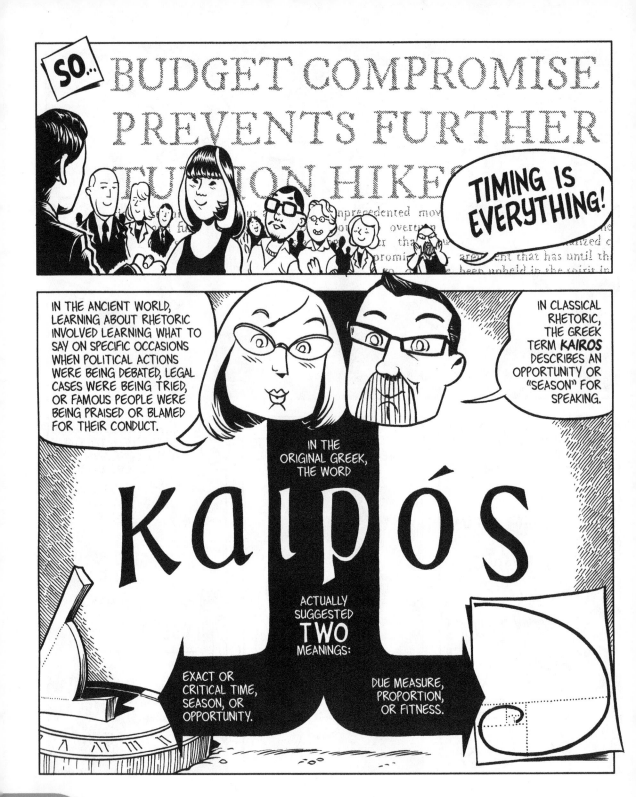

Panel 1:

KAIROS WORKS IN MANY WAYS, ESPECIALLY TODAY.

DIGITAL WRITERS WHO COMMUNICATE USING THEIR COMPUTERS OR MOBILE PHONES OFTEN FEEL COMPELLED TO HIT "SEND" OR "ENTER" AS RAPIDLY AS POSSIBLE TO KEEP UP WITH A FAST-MOVING ONLINE CONVERSATION.

EMAIL

to: PREZ   subj: LISTEN, YO

WARNING! MESSAGE CONTAINS FORCEFUL LANGUAGE

I NEED TO SEND THIS EMAIL RIGHT AWAY TO THE PRESIDENT OF THE UNIVERSITY.

Panel 2:

BUT IT'S USUALLY BETTER FIRST TO CONSIDER BOTH THE APPROPRIATENESS OF YOUR MESSAGE **AND** THE TIMING OF YOUR REPLY.

DING!

EMAIL

to: PREZ   subj: LISTEN, YOU

SEND ANYWAY

&%$#@!

I HIT "SEND" BEFORE I MEANT TO!

Panel 3:

WRITERS OFTEN MISS THE LONG-TERM **APPROPRIATENESS** OF KAIROS WHEN THEY FOCUS ON THE IN-THE-MOMENT **RESPONSIVENESS** OF KAIROS.

IF YOU THINK ABOUT A RHETORICAL OCCASION **ONLY** IN TERMS OF REACTING QUICKLY, YOU COULD EASILY END UP WITH AN EMBARRASSING DISASTER.

EMAIL

to: PREZ   subj: LISTEN, YOU

YOUR MESSAGE HAS BEEN IRRETRIEVABLY SENT.

TENURE

Liz's Boyfriend is on the prowl.

Ladies like this

Liz's Boyfriend
Relationship Status:
FINALLY SINGLE!

Plato: I ... my bro, w... nd time f... t?

Aristotle: want to ... tonig...

FOR EXAMPLE, USERS OF SOCIAL NETWORK SITES OFTEN ANNOUNCE CHANGES IN RELATIONSHIP STATUS...

...OFTEN BEFORE THEIR **PARTNERS** ARE INFORMED.

ON THE OTHER HAND, WAITING TOO **LONG** CAN DOOM YOUR COMMUNICATION EFFORTS.

HAPPY V-DAY!

KISS ME I'M IRISH

MARCH

17

SOMETIMES, HOWEVER, PEOPLE MANAGE TO SAY THE RIGHT THING AT JUST THE RIGHT MOMENT, AND THOSE PARTICULARLY **APT** WORDS ARE REMEMBERED FOR **CENTURIES.**

FAMOUS LAST WORDS -- SUCH AS NATHAN HALE'S

"I only regret that I have but one life to lose for my country."

-- ARE STILL QUOTED TODAY.

THE ROMAN RHETORICIAN **MARCUS TULLIUS CICERO** REALLY UNDERSTOOD THE IMPORTANCE OF KAIROS.

FOR EXAMPLE, WHEN HE WAS ABOUT TO BE EXECUTED ON ARBITRARY POLITICAL GROUNDS HE SAW A MOMENT FOR GRACIOUS WIT:

"There is nothing proper about what you are doing, soldier...

"...but at least make sure you cut off my head properly."

AFTER ALL, ARISTOTLE WASN'T THE **ONLY** FAMOUS RHETORICIAN IN THE ANCIENT WORLD.

CICERO, WHO LIKE MANY CULTURED ROMANS **ADMIRED** THE ANCIENT GREEKS, TRAINED ORATORS FOR THE ROMAN **SENATE**.

"No one can speak well, unless he thoroughly understands his subject."

CICERO (106–43 BCE)
ANCIENT ROMAN PHILOSOPHER, LAWYER, AND STATESMAN

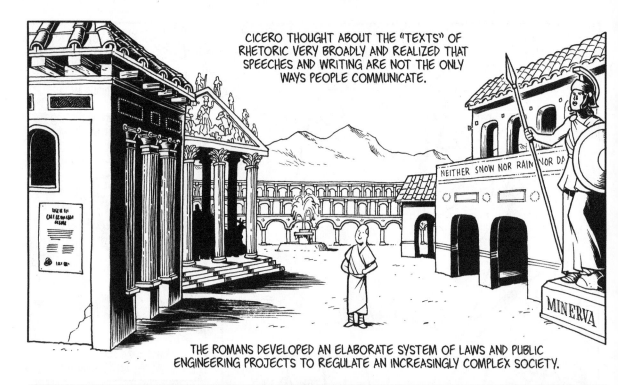

CICERO THOUGHT ABOUT THE "TEXTS" OF RHETORIC VERY BROADLY AND REALIZED THAT SPEECHES AND WRITING ARE NOT THE ONLY WAYS PEOPLE COMMUNICATE.

THE ROMANS DEVELOPED AN ELABORATE SYSTEM OF LAWS AND PUBLIC ENGINEERING PROJECTS TO REGULATE AN INCREASINGLY COMPLEX SOCIETY.

THESE **RES PUBLICA**, OR "PUBLIC THINGS," ARE WORTH CONSIDERING AS RHETORICAL ACTS AND SPACES.

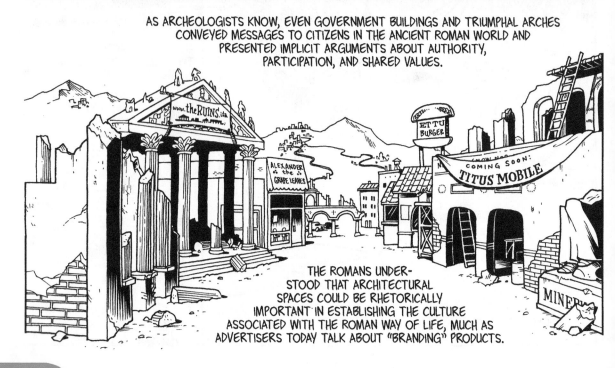

AS ARCHEOLOGISTS KNOW, EVEN GOVERNMENT BUILDINGS AND TRIUMPHAL ARCHES CONVEYED MESSAGES TO CITIZENS IN THE ANCIENT ROMAN WORLD AND PRESENTED IMPLICIT ARGUMENTS ABOUT AUTHORITY, PARTICIPATION, AND SHARED VALUES.

THE ROMANS UNDERSTOOD THAT ARCHITECTURAL SPACES COULD BE RHETORICALLY IMPORTANT IN ESTABLISHING THE CULTURE ASSOCIATED WITH THE ROMAN WAY OF LIFE, MUCH AS ADVERTISERS TODAY TALK ABOUT "BRANDING" PRODUCTS.

WE STILL NEED SPACES TO DEBATE IMPORTANT ISSUES IN PUBLIC.

AND KNOWING SPECIAL LANGUAGE FROM THE FIELD OF RHETORIC CAN BE HELPFUL TO IDENTIFY EFFECTIVE -- AND INEFFECTIVE -- TECHNIQUES.

GREEK TERMS LIKE *ETHOS, LOGOS, PATHOS,* AND *KAIROS* MIGHT NOT BE WORDS THAT YOU ADD TO YOUR EVERYDAY VOCABULARY.

BUT YOU USE THE GENERAL CONCEPTS ALL THE TIME...

...IN PERSON AND ONLINE.

and Jonathan

Aristotle: haha nice hairstyle LOL

Plato: If you saw where the rain came from, you could never go back to your happy ignorance !!!!

Cicero: As the mature

REFRAME with Luis & Cindy

What does ARISTOTLE have to do with ME?

REMEMBER WHEN WE TALKED ABOUT **ETHOS** IN CLASS?

YOU DON'T MAKE YOURSELF SOUND LIKE SOMEONE WHO HAS A GOOD REASON TO BE EXCUSED. IN FACT, YOU SOUND LIKE KIND OF A JERK.

AND REMEMBER, YOU'RE ASKING FOR A **FAVOR** FROM YOUR PROFESSOR. BUT YOUR EMAIL SOUNDS LIKE YOU'RE ADDRESSING ANOTHER **STUDENT**, NOT YOUR TEACHER.

THAT COULD BE A BIG MISTAKE.

YOU NEED AN APPEAL TO **PATHOS** -- TO MAKE HER FEEL A CERTAIN WAY, RIGHT? BUT YOUR SUPER-CASUAL APPROACH MIGHT EARN YOU A RE-ACTION YOU DON'T WANT.

AND DON'T FORGET **LOGOS** -- ORGANIZ-ING WHAT YOU WANT TO SAY INTO A COMPELLING ARGUMENT OR STORY.

REASONS APOLOGIES EXCUSES PLANS EXPLANATIONS

KAIROS PATHOS ETHOS

WOW, YOU **WERE** REALLY PAYING ATTENTION IN CLASS!

BUT I SEE WHAT YOU MEAN. LET ME TRY MAKING IT A BIT MORE LIKE A FORMAL LETTER.

TO: l.losh@univ.edu
SUBJECT: Upcoming Absence

Dear Dr. Losh,

My older brother is on active duty in the military and is being deployed this month. My extended family will have his going-away party on Friday. I'd very much like to be there, given the circumstances. May I be excused from class? I'll be happy to make up any work, and I will ask my classmates for notes.

Sincerely,

Luis

TO: luis@univ.edu
SUBJECT: RE: Upcoming Absence

Dear Luis,

Thanks for the heads-up. We'll be starting brainstorming and process work on your first assignment, an analysis of the design of a print advertisement for an on-campus organization, service, or cause.

You should analyze the rhetorical strategies of the advertisement by commenting on its logos, pathos, ethos, and kairos. You should study details in the wording, images, typography, organization, and visual design on the page. Let me know if you have any questions, and I'll see you in class on Monday.

Best,
Liz

I SEE WHAT YOU MEAN -- THEY ARE TOTALLY DIFFERENT.

WE CAN START WITH THESE QUESTIONS:

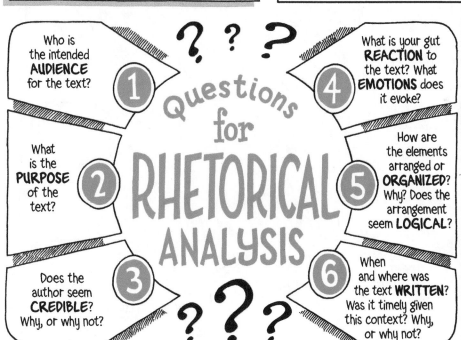

Questions for **RHETORICAL ANALYSIS**

1 Who is the intended **AUDIENCE** for the text?

2 What is the **PURPOSE** of the text?

3 Does the author seem **CREDIBLE**? Why, or why not?

4 What is your gut **REACTION** to the text? What **EMOTIONS** does it evoke?

5 How are the elements arranged or **ORGANIZED**? Why? Does the arrangement seem **LOGICAL**?

6 When and where was the text **WRITTEN**? Was it timely given this context? Why, or why not?

QUICK REVIEW:

ETHOS
The credibility that a speaker/writer brings to a subject.

PATHOS
Use of emotion in debate/argument.

LOGOS
Appeal to reason, to the forcefulness of a well-thought-out and well-argued position.

JOIN US AT AN **INFORMATIONAL LUNCHEON** TO

 Get a HEAD START on building your RÉSUMÉ!

 Learn new SKILLS!

NETWORK with potential COLLEAGUES and EMPLOYERS!

SPONSORED BY

BETA BETA BETA

Monday, November 2nd
11 am – 1 pm

[No shorts or Jeans, Please!]

Issue 1 • Why Rhetoric?

COMING UP IN THE NEXT EXCITING EPISODE OF **REFRAME**

"How do I READ this?"

[pg 107]

WALK the TALK

1 What's the RHETORICAL SITUATION?

AN ACADEMIC ARTICLE OFTEN NEEDS AN ABSTRACT LIKE THIS ONE.

I WROTE THIS FOR AN ESSAY ABOUT PRESIDENT OBAMA'S USE OF SOCIAL MEDIA.

AN ACADEMIC ABSTRACT NEEDS TO SUMMARIZE THE MAIN POINT OF THE ARTICLE AND SHOW WHY THE ARTICLE IS IMPORTANT.

COMPARATIVE AMERICAN STUDIES · ELIZABETH LOSH

ABSTRACT

"The persuasive power of social network sites, blogs, Twitter, and SMS messages was obviously important for the Obama campaign and subsequent presidency in associating him with youth, technology, volunteerism, and user-generated content. The conventional wisdom is that Obama has been a user of social media who models to other heads of state ways to disseminate political messages successfully without notable incidents of stalled reception or public disgrace. However, since taking office, Obama's abandonment of YouTube public diplomacy efforts and White House online town halls might represent him as imitating pre-digital presidents like Kennedy and Reagan."

Comparative American Studies

How does the WRITER USE PATHOS?

NOTING THAT OBAMA'S USE OF SOCIAL MEDIA ASSOCIATES HIM "WITH YOUTH, TECHNOLOGY, VOLUNTEERISM" MAY APPEAL TO READERS' EMOTIONS. IN OUR CULTURE, THOSE ATTRIBUTES ARE USUALLY SEEN AS POSITIVE.

SOME RHETORICAL SITUATIONS CALL FOR PATHOS -- BUT AN ABSTRACT MAY NOT DEVOTE MUCH SPACE TO SUCH APPEALS. AFTER ALL, THE GOAL HERE IS TO SUMMARIZE.

DRAWING CONCLUSIONS

The following assignments ask you to practice thinking about the rhetorical strategies of **ETHOS, LOGOS, PATHOS,** and **KAIROS.**

1 Keep your eye out for published texts around campus: newspapers, flyers, posters, zines, etc. When you find an interesting one, grab a copy or take a picture of it.

Who is producing the text, and for whom? What does the text aim to do, how does it do it, and how effectively does it do it? Why might this text exist on your college campus? (Luis and Cindy perform a similar analysis in the Reframe; how does the text you've found compare to the ones they've found?)

2 Jot down some ideas about the rhetorical characteristics of informal and formal writing. In what ways are they similar? In what key ways are they different?

Then, pick a kind of formal writing that you either are working on now or have encountered in the past.

Think about how a consideration of logos, ethos, pathos, and kairos could help you compose a formal piece better.

3 The Internet brings together diverse groups of people and invites them to share their ideas and opinions, so conflicts, disagreements, and arguments are common online.

Find a contentious or polemical exchange on one of your favorite Internet haunts. Dissect the appeals used by the various parties in the exchange. Look specifically for places where people lean on their reputation or expertise (ethos), where the participants solicit specific emotional responses from one another or from their audiences (pathos), and where logic, facts, or evidence are used (logos). What are the effects of using the appeals? Whose arguments are most convincing in this exchange, and why?

4 Your classmate has just heard that your instructor plans to test students on this chapter by requiring in-class essays summarizing the content, closed book.

In whatever text you see fit -- an email, a text message, an open letter, a social media rant, a formal letter to your instructor or someone else -- try to stop this in-class essay from happening!

Consider the rhetorical occasion and the context, and compose -- alone or with your classmates -- an effective rhetorical response. What appeals will be most effective for your audience? What genre feels most kairotic?

WHEN WE READ WE OFTEN SEE PICTURES IN OUR **MINDS**.

FOR EXAMPLE...

FREDERICK DOUGLASS (1818 - 1895) American Abolitioni... Orator, and Editor

...TAKE THIS PASSAGE FROM AN **EARLY VERSION** OF THE AUTOBIOGRAPHY OF FREDERICK DOUGLASS, WHO DESCRIBES HIS EXPERIENCES AS AN **ESCAPED SLAVE**.

WE'VE BROKEN UP THE WORDS SO THAT INDIVIDUAL PASSAGES ARE ILLUSTRATED, AS THEY MIGHT BE IN A READER'S IMAGINATION, TO MAKE SOME POINTS ABOUT A PROCESS KNOWN AS

CRITICAL READING!

"I have been frequently asked how I felt when I found myself in a free State. I have never been able to answer the question with any satisfaction to myself."

"It was a moment of the highest excitement I ever experienced."

WHAT'S THE DIFFERENCE IN EFFECT BETWEEN "HIGHEST EXCITEMENT" AND "GREATEST EXCITEMENT"?

I THINK "HIGHEST" IS A LOT MORE VIVID -- "HIGH" EVOKES AN ELEVATION IN STATUS, IN THIS CASE FROM SLAVE TO FREE CITIZEN.

"I suppose I felt as one may imagine the unarmed mariner to feel when he is rescued by a friendly man-of-war from the pursuit of a pirate."

"But the loneliness overcame me. There I was in the midst of thousands, and yet a perfect stranger; without home and without friends, in the midst of thousands of my own brethren—children of a common Father...

INTERESTING THAT HE SAYS "BRETHREN" AND "A COMMON **FATHER**" INSTEAD OF "BROTHERS AND SISTERS" OR "A COMMON **MOTHER**"?

IT COULD JUST BE A **GUY** THING.

...LET'S COME BACK TO THAT LATER.

"...and yet I dared not to unfold to any one of them my sad condition. I was afraid to speak to any one for fear of speaking to the wrong one...

"...and thereby falling into the hands of money-loving kidnappers, whose business it was to lie in wait for the panting fugitive...

"...as the ferocious beasts of the forest lie in wait for their prey."

"The motto which I adopted when I started from slavery was this—'Trust no man!'"

"I saw in every white man an enemy...

"...and in almost every colored man cause for distrust.

"It was a most painful situation;...

"...and, to understand it, one must needs experience it, or imagine himself in similar circumstances."

"Let him be a fugitive slave in a strange land—

—a land given up to be the hunting-ground for slaveholders—

"whose inhabitants are legalized kidnappers—

—where he is every moment subjected to the terrible liability of being seized upon by his fellowmen,"

"as the hideous crocodile seizes upon his prey!—"

YOU CAN READ DOUGLASS'S BOOK AND SEE IT AS A SEQUENCE OF IMAGES--

--A WAY OF IMAGINING THE DIFFERENT SPACES...

...IN WHICH DOUGLASS EXPERIENCED THE TRIALS...

...THAT SHAPED HIS LIFE.

YOU CAN ENJOY THE BOOK FOR ITS GRIPPING SCENES...

...AND JUST LET YOURSELF BE TAKEN IN BY DOUGLASS'S HORRIFIC AND MOVING STORY...

GASP!

SHH!

FREDERICK DOUGLASS

...OR YOU CAN READ ACTIVELY AND TURN YOUR ATTENTION TO PARTICULAR ASPECTS OF DOUGLASS'S LANGUAGE OR LOGIC.

FOR EXAMPLE...

...YOU MIGHT NOTICE A BIBLICAL ALLUSION TO THE STORY OF DANIEL IN THE LION'S DEN, WHICH IS FROM THE OLD TESTAMENT.

BIBLE

COMPREHENSIVE CRITICAL READING MAY REQUIRE YOU TO SEARCH FOR SPECIALIZED CONCEPTS IN A WRITER'S WORK....

...BUT THE GENERAL STRATEGIES THAT FOLLOW CAN SERVE YOU WELL WHEN YOU READ ANY TEXT.

SOMETIMES YOU ARE CONSIDERING IF THE LANGUAGE IS **EXTREME**.

HYPERBOLE!!! VS. understatement.

SOMETIMES YOU ARE LOOKING FOR INFORMATION THAT THE AUTHOR HAS **OMITTED**.

SOMETIMES YOU ARE LOOKING FOR **UNCLEAR** OR **AMBIGUOUS** LANGUAGE --

-- WHAT IS **DIFFICULT** TO INTERPRET RATHER THAN WHAT IS **EASY**.

READING IN THIS WAY... ...IS CALLED **ANALYSIS**.

a·nàl·y·sis

THE WORD ANALYSIS COMES FROM THE **GREEK** AND MEANS, LITERALLY, A PROCESS OF "UNLOOSENING."

THIS IS A **USEFUL** WAY TO THINK ABOUT THE **PROCESS** OF ANALYSIS.

ANALYSIS REQUIRES YOU TO TAKE WHAT SEEMS LIKE A UNIFIED, COHERENT OBJECT AND BREAK IT UP INTO **PIECES**.

ALTHOUGH ANALYSIS IS THOUGHT OF AS AN ACTIVITY THAT RESEARCHERS DO IN **SCIENTIFIC LABORATORIES**...

...SCHOLARS WHO STUDY **LITERARY, HISTORICAL,** OR **PHILOSOPHICAL** TEXTS DO IT TOO.

BLOOD

OXYGEN · NITROGEN · CARBON DIOXIDE · HYDROGEN · IRON

DICTION · ALLUSIONS · THEMES

BOOK

YOU CAN DO THE **SAME THING** WITH THIS TEXT. SUPPOSE YOU TOOK ALL OF DOUGLASS'S IMAGES OF **WILD ANIMALS** -- AND **WILD MEN** -- FROM THE PASSAGE PRESENTED EARLIER AND **SEPARATED THEM OUT** FROM THE REST OF THE TEXT.

FOCUSING ON THIS KIND OF LANGUAGE WITH **ANIMAL IMAGERY** MIGHT HELP YOU UNDERSTAND THE PREDATORY NATURE OF **SLAVERY**, AND HOW THE INSTITUTION OF SLAVERY TREATS HUMANS LIKE **ANIMALS**.

ABOLITIONIST IMAGERY

OR YOU COULD LOCATE ALL THE TIMES THAT DOUGLASS TALKS ABOUT HOW HE FELT BUT CREATES SOME **SEPARATION** FROM THE EVENTS THAT HE IS RECORDING.

York, I said I felt like
d. I suppose I felt as one ma
imagine the unarmed mariner to feel whe
he is rescued by a friendly man-of-war from the pursuit

OFTEN HE DOES THIS BY ADDING MORE **EMOTIONAL DISTANCE** WITH EXTRA VERBS ABOUT **"SAYING"** OR **"SUPPOSING"** IN RELATION TO HIS FEELINGS.

WRITERS SOMETIMES LEAVE **IMPLICIT** MESSAGES IN THEIR TEXTS -- FROM THE LATIN *IMPLICARE*, MEANING "TO ENFOLD."

WRITE WRITE

FOR EXAMPLE, WHEN DOUGLASS CREATES **SEPARATION** FROM HIMSELF AND HIS DESCRIPTION OF SLAVERY, HE IS TRYING TO ESTABLISH HIMSELF AS AN **OBJECTIVE OBSERVER** OF SLAVERY, NOT JUST A **VICTIM** OF IT.

STUFF STUFF

FREDERICK DOUGLASS

THE **IMPLICIT MESSAGE** HERE IS THAT WE CAN **TRUST** DOUGLASS.

ANOTHER WAY TO THINK ABOUT CRITICAL READING IS TO THINK ABOUT IT AS **EXPLICATION**.

to **EXPLICATE** is to **UNFOLD**

THE WORD **EXPLICATION** COMES FROM THE LATIN EXPLICARE, WHICH MEANS "TO UNFOLD."

EXPLICATION IS THE PROCESS OF **REVEALING** OR **UNCOVERING** IDEAS OR BELIEFS BURIED IN THE TEXT.

DOUGLASS'S PREJUDICES ABOUT CITIES

DOUGLASS'S IDEAS ABOUT THE NATURAL WORLD

DOUGLASS'S ATTITUDES ABOUT AFRICA

THESE IDEAS ARE NOT OBVIOUS; THEY ARE ONLY **SUGGESTED**, PERHAPS **INDIRECTLY**, BY THE TEXT.

FOR INSTANCE, DOUGLASS COMPARES POTENTIAL KIDNAPPERS TO "HIDEOUS **CROCODILES.**"

DOUGLASS WAS WELL AWARE THAT MANY CONSIDERED SLAVES TO BE **ANIMALS.** IN A NICE **REVERSAL,** HIS METAPHOR OF THE CROCODILE IMPLIES THAT **SLAVEHOLDERS** REALLY ARE THE BEASTS.

IF YOU REMEMBER WHAT WE LEARNED ABOUT **PATHOS, LOGOS, ETHOS,** AND **KAIROS** YOU CAN SEE THAT THOSE ARE ALSO AT WORK HERE.

OBVIOUSLY, DOUGLASS IS TRYING TO STIR HIS AUDIENCE'S **EMOTIONS,** BY USING LANGUAGE THAT SUGGESTS THAT **PITY AND FEAR** ARE APPROPRIATE RESPONSES TO HIS TEXT.

THE IMAGES THAT WE MIGHT REMEMBER BEST ARE THE IMAGES OF **EXOTIC SCENES, WILD ANIMALS,** AND **SAVAGE PEOPLES,** WHICH ARE DESIGNED TO EXCITE OUR **EMOTIONS.**

TRUST NO MAN

PATHOS

WE CAN ALSO SEE THAT DOUGLASS IS MAKING A NUMBER OF **LOGICAL COMPARISONS** OF SEEMINGLY UNLIKE THINGS.

HE DESCRIBES SLAVE TRADERS AS **BEASTLY**...

...AND HE NOTES THAT ESCAPED SLAVES MIGHT FIND NEW YORK CITY TO BE AS MUCH A PART OF THE SYSTEM OF TERROR AS THE SLAVE-HOLDING **SOUTH**.

HE IS WRITING ABOUT A SUPPOSEDLY CIVILIZED COUNTRY, **AMERICA**, NOT A PLACE LIKE AFRICA, WHICH MANY IN THE UNITED STATES IMAGINED TO BE **VIOLENT** AND **WILD**.

LOGOS

THERE ARE ALSO MANY POINTS IN THIS PASSAGE WHERE DOUGLASS IS CONCERNED WITH HIS **AUTHORITY**, AS A SPEAKER AND WRITER.

HE WAS "**FREQUENTLY ASKED**" HOW HE FELT ABOUT BEING FREE IN NEW YORK, WHICH IMPLIES THAT HIS OPINION WAS SOUGHT BY **MANY**.

ETHOS

83

SYNTHESIS INVOLVES MAKING MEANING FROM MULTIPLE SOURCES.

FOR EXAMPLE, THERE WASN'T JUST **ONE** EDITION OF DOUGLASS'S BOOK.

...THERE WERE **MANY!**

AND, AS DOUGLASS TOLD HIS LIFE STORY, IT GOT A LOT **LONGER.**

THE FIRST VERSION OF HIS BOOK WAS JUST 124 PAGES.

BY THE END OF HIS LIFE, WHEN HE WROTE *THE LIFE AND TIMES OF FREDERICK DOUGLASS,* HIS AUTOBIOGRAPHY HAD GROWN TO OVER **700 PAGES.**

THAT'S A LOT OF MATERIAL TO **SYNTHESIZE!**

THAT'S NOT **ALL.**

THERE WERE ALSO **ILLUSTRATIONS** IN DOUGLASS'S BOOKS THAT WE MIGHT WANT TO **ANALYZE** AND THEN **SYNTHESIZE.**

85

AFTER ALL, ACCORDING TO **EYEWITNESSES**, THE REAL-LIFE DOUGLASS WAS ABOUT **SIX FEET TALL** AND VERY PHYSICALLY **IMPOSING**.

DOUGLASS WAS DEEPLY CONCERNED ABOUT THE WAY ILLUSTRATIONS IN BOOKS DEPICTED HIM.

BUT WE NEED TO DO SOME MORE **SYNTHESIS** TO PROVE THAT THESIS.

HERE'S A CLUE.

IN 1849 DOUGLASS PRAISED AN **ILLUSTRATED BOOK** ABOUT FAMOUS AFRICAN AMERICANS.

IN THE REVIEW, HE ALSO **RIDICULED** AN ILLUSTRATION OF HIMSELF, WHICH HE SAID HAD A

"much more kindly and amiable expression, than is generally thought to characterize the face of a fugitive slave."

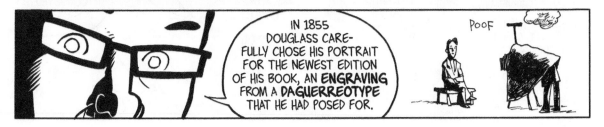

IN 1855 DOUGLASS CAREFULLY CHOSE HIS PORTRAIT FOR THE NEWEST EDITION OF HIS BOOK, AN **ENGRAVING** FROM A **DAGUERREOTYPE** THAT HE HAD POSED FOR.

POOF

(Photo, 1845) New York Historical Society

BY **ASSEMBLING INFORMATION FROM MULTIPLE SOURCES**, WE CAN REALLY SAY SOMETHING INTERESTING ABOUT A WORK AND HOW TO READ IT CRITICALLY --

-- EVEN ONE THAT PEOPLE THINK THAT THEY ALREADY KNOW **WELL**, LIKE DOUGLASS'S AUTOBIOGRAPHY.

WITH SOMEONE LIKE DOUGLASS THERE MIGHT BE A LOT OF MATERIAL TO SYNTHESIZE.

LET'S GO BACK TO THE **ORIGINAL BOOK** AND ITS 124 PAGES.

YOU CAN DO SYNTHESIS THERE, TOO.

SOMETIMES A SINGLE BOOK IS ACTUALLY MADE UP OF **MANY KINDS OF SOURCES.**

LOOKING AT THE **SOURCES** THAT A WRITER USES MAY GIVE US CLUES THAT LEAD TO **ADDITIONAL INFORMATION.**

THEN WE NEED TO BRING ALL THAT MATERIAL TOGETHER AND SUPPORT A **THESIS** ABOUT WHAT IT ALL ADDS UP TO MEAN.

BIBLICAL PASSAGES

PHILOSOPHICAL SNIPPETS

LETTERS

PREFACES

POEMS

MAPS

ILLUSTRATIONS

BOOKS FROM OUR **OWN** TIME OFTEN CONTAIN A LOT OF DIFFERENT KINDS OF TEXTS **TOO.**

A **CELEBRITY BIOGRAPHY** MIGHT INCLUDE **NEWSPAPER STORIES** OR EVEN **BEAUTY TIPS** AND **RECIP**--!

?!?

SNATCH!

I CAN'T TAKE YOU **ANYWHERE.**

WHEN DOUGLASS'S BOOK INITIALLY APPEARED, SOME DOUBTED ITS **AUTHENTICITY**.

THEY THOUGHT THAT FUGITIVE SLAVES **EXAGGERATED** THEIR STORIES OR THAT AFRICAN AMERICANS WEREN'T **LITERATE** ENOUGH TO WRITE ANYTHING DOWN.

PROMINENT MEN ATTESTED TO DOUGLASS'S **LITERACY** AND **HONEST CHARACTER** IN LETTERS INCLUDED AT THE FRONT OF HIS BOOK.

THEY WEREN'T **CO-AUTHORS** OF HIS BOOK, BUT THEY WERE **FELLOW WRITERS** IN IT.

THESE PEOPLE THOUGHT THAT ACCOUNTS FROM FUGITIVE SLAVES MUST REALLY BE THE **FICTIONS** OF WHITE **ABOLITIONISTS**.

DOES THIS MEAN THAT I NEED TO FIND OUT MORE ABOUT **WILLIAM LLOYD GARRISON** AND **WENDELL PHILLIPS**?

THIS IS **WAY TOO MUCH TO SYNTHESIZE** FOR A THREE- TO FIVE-PAGE **PAPER**!

WHEN DOES IT **STOP**?

THE SECRET TO DOING **SYNTHESIS** IS FOCUSING ON **MANAGEABLE** TASKS.

HERE, LET ME GIVE YOU ONE MORE EXAMPLE.

NOT **ANOTHER** EXAMPLE!

RELAX. THIS ONE HAS **PICTURES**.

OKAY.

I LIKE THE EXAMPLES WITH PICTURES.

91

JONATHAN, WHAT DO YOU MEAN BY "CRITICAL LENSES"?

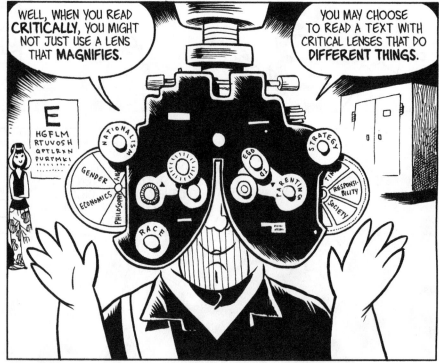

WELL, WHEN YOU READ **CRITICALLY**, YOU MIGHT NOT JUST USE A LENS THAT **MAGNIFIES**.

YOU MAY CHOOSE TO READ A TEXT WITH CRITICAL LENSES THAT DO **DIFFERENT THINGS**.

SOMETIMES YOU MIGHT FIND IT IS INTERESTING TO VIEW A TEXT THROUGH **ANOTHER** TEXT OR PERSPECTIVE.

FOR **EXAMPLE**...

GEND-O-VISION

...I MIGHT CHOOSE TO READ A TEXT FROM THE PERSPECTIVE OF **GENDER** -- TO **APPLY** THE CONCEPT OF GENDER TO MY READING OF THE TEXT.

FOR INSTANCE, I MIGHT ASK HOW DOUGLASS REPRESENTS **FEMALE SLAVES**.

DOES HE DESCRIBE **DIFFERENCES** IN THE TREATMENT OF **MEN** AND **WOMEN** AS SLAVES?

YOU CAN READ A BOOK AS THOUGH YOU ARE READING IT **THROUGH** ANOTHER BOOK --

-- **APPLYING** THE IDEAS, PHILOSOPHY, OR METHODS OF ANALYSIS FROM ONE TEXT TO ANOTHER.

SOMETIMES YOU READ A TEXT **SIDE BY SIDE** WITH ANOTHER TEXT, NOTING THE SIMILARITIES AND DIFFERENCES BETWEEN THE TWO.

WRITING TEACHERS CALL THIS "**COMPARISON** AND **CONTRAST**."

AUTOBIOGRAPHY of FREDERICK DOUGLASS

LETTER from BIRMINGHAM JAIL — MARTIN LUTHER KING JR.

COMPARISON HAS BEEN PART OF RHETORICAL INSTRUCTION SINCE ANCIENT TIMES. IT'S AN IMPORTANT KIND OF **SYNTHESIS** IN CRITICAL READING.

IN **HUMANITIES** CLASSES, ESSAY EXAMINATIONS USUALLY ASK **COMPARISON** AND **CONTRAST** QUESTIONS, BUT THEY SOMETIMES POSE **APPLICATION** QUESTIONS AS WELL.

Compare the text of Douglass's narrative to Olaudah Equiano's slave narrative, which was written many years earlier. Both men were abolitionist speakers who urged the passage of antislavery legislation in the United States and in Great Britain respectively, but they had very different rhetorical techniques. How do they describe captivity and injustice? How do they describe their literacy and public speaking?

Apply W. E. B. DuBois's theory of "double consciousness" to the text of Frederick Douglass's Narrative. In what ways does Douglass seem to experience double consciousness as he interacts with both white and black participants in his story?

WHEN I **COMPARE AND CONTRAST** TWO TEXTS...

...I START BY MAKING LISTS OF HOW THEY'RE ALIKE AND HOW THEY'RE DIFFERENT.

WITH **APPLICATION** QUESTIONS...

...I CAN APPLY THE THEORETICAL TEXTS I'M READING TO NEW **SITUATIONS**.

FOR INSTANCE, I MIGHT APPLY IDEAS FROM **PLATO** AND **ARISTOTLE** TO A GRAPHIC NOVEL I READ FOR A LIT CLASS.

IMAGING IDEAL READERS

THERE'S **ANOTHER** KIND OF CREATIVE EXERCISE THAT INVOLVES CRITICAL READING.

IT INVOLVES THINKING ABOUT **IDEAL READERS** WHEN EXAMINING A TEXT.

DOUGLASS IS MAKING A VERY **SPECIFIC** RHETORICAL APPEAL TO THE READER TO IDENTIFY WITH HIS PLIGHT IN **NEW YORK**...

...EVEN THOUGH THE SITUATION OF A **FUGITIVE SLAVE** MAY SEEM FAR REMOVED FROM THE CONCERNS OF HIS PRIVILEGED WHITE **AUDIENCES**.

HE IS **ALSO** URGING HIS READERS TO BE **SELF-CRITICAL** AND TO CONSIDER INJUSTICE DONE TO OTHERS THAT IS CLOSER TO HOME THAN THEY MIGHT **REALIZE**.

"GOOD"

"BAD"

TO HELP PERSUADE OTHERS, WRITERS OFTEN IMAGINE AN **IDEAL READER**.

AS HE WROTE, DOUGLASS PROBABLY CONSIDERED HOW A PERSON FROM HIS OWN **TIME** BUT OF A **DIFFERENT RACE** MIGHT READ HIS BOOK.

"I say, let him place himself in my situation—without home or friends—without money or credit—wanting shelter, and no one to give it—wanting bread, and no money to buy it,

"—and at the same time let him feel that he is pursued by merciless men-hunters..."

"—perfectly helpless both as to the means of defence and means of escape,

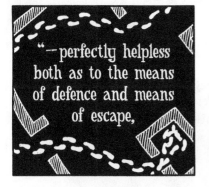

"—in the midst of plenty, yet suffering the terrible gnawings of hunger,—in the midst of houses, yet having no home,

"—among fellow-men, yet feeling as if in the midst of wild beasts, whose greediness to swallow up the trembling and half-famished fugitive is only equalled by that with which the monsters of the deep swallow up the helpless fish upon which they subsist,"

YOUR IDEAL READER FOR THE ESSAYS THAT YOU WRITE IN **COLLEGE** MAY BE VERY MUCH LIKE **YOURSELF**, PARTICULARLY IF YOU ARE PREPARING SOMETHING TO BE READ BY A GROUP OF **PEERS**.

OR YOUR IDEAL READER MIGHT BE MORE OF AN **EXPERT** ON THE SUBJECT TO WHOM YOU WILL WANT TO DEMONSTRATE YOUR **MASTERY** OF THE COURSE MATERIAL.

PEER   YOU   PROFESSOR   PUBLIC

IT IS ALWAYS HELPFUL TO ENVISION A READER **APPROPRIATE** TO A GIVEN PURPOSE AND TO THE PARTICULAR RHETORICAL OCCASION OR **KAIROS**.

YOU MAY THINK YOU DON'T KNOW ENOUGH ABOUT **FREDERICK DOUGLASS** OR THE **PRE-CIVIL WAR PERIOD** IN U.S. HISTORY TO UNDERSTAND WHAT DOUGLASS WANTED READERS TO KNOW.

BUT ANY READER WHO PAYS ATTENTION AND USES SMART READING STRATEGIES CAN LEARN TO EXPLICATE A TEXT AND UNCOVER MEANINGS.

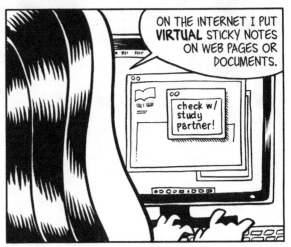

Reading on the Internet offers opportunities to interact with texts and writers.

Many Web sites offer links to free social bookmarking tools that let you share what you are reading with friends.

thanks! =-)

I'M **CONFUSED** HERE.

WHEN I'M CONFUSED, SOMETIMES I LOOK THINGS UP ON THE WEB.

BUT IT IS TRUE THAT IF YOU ARE GOING TO USE THE MATERIAL FROM THE WEB IN A **WRITING ASSIGNMENT**, YOU SHOULD CHECK TO SEE IF IT COMES FROM A RELIABLE **SOURCE*** --

-- A SOURCE WRITTEN BY **RECOGNIZED EXPERTS** WITH THE AUTHORITY TO SPEAK OR WRITE ABOUT AN ISSUE.

* For more on research, see CHAPTER 6.

AND YOU'LL NEED TO EVALUATE THE SOURCE NO MATTER **WHERE** YOU FIND IT.

DON'T BE AFRAID TO TALK TO YOUR INSTRUCTORS AS WELL.

the PROF

YOU CAN **ALSO** ASK OTHER PEOPLE FOR HELP WITH A DIFFICULT PASSAGE.

BOOK CLUB

TRADITIONALLY, READING HAS BEEN A SOCIAL PROCESS IN WHICH WE SHARE OUR EXPERIENCES OF READING WITH **OTHERS**.

IN THE EIGHTEENTH AND NINE-TEENTH **CENTURIES**, PEOPLE OFTEN SHARED **BOOKS** AND **NEWSPAPERS** WITH FRIENDS, AND FAMILIES READ **OUT LOUD** TOGETHER EACH NIGHT.

SOME **LITERACY SPECIALISTS** SAY THAT EVEN TODAY READING ALOUD ISN'T JUST FOR **KIDS**.

THE MORE THAT STUDENTS UNDERSTAND THAT READING IS A **PUBLIC** AND **SOCIAL ACTIVITY**, THE MORE THEY **IMPROVE**.

SOMETIMES I NEED TO GO OVER A PAGE MORE THAN **ONCE**.

GOOD READERS AREN'T NECESSARILY **FAST** READERS.

AND YOU MIGHT SEE SOMETHING IN A TEXT THAT ANOTHER STUDENT **DOESN'T** SEE.

THANKS, I THINK THAT --

WOW!

SEE?

REFRAME with **Luis & Cindy**

How do I **READ** this?

beep beep boop

bleep-a-bloop!

ARE YOU STILL UP?

YES, I'M FINISHING UP SOME OF THE READING.

ME TOO, I'M REALLY **BEHIND**. WHEN I WENT HOME FOR MY BROTHER'S SEND-OFF, IT WAS HARD TO FIND ANY TIME FOR **SCHOOLWORK**. IT WAS NEVER REALLY QUIET ENOUGH TO CONCENTRATE.

WHEN I CAME BACK FROM MY TRIP, I FIGURED THAT THESE WERE JUST COMIC BOOKS AND THAT I COULD SPEED-READ THEM, BUT THIS IS TAKING **FOREVER**.

YEAH, COMIC BOOKS AREN'T ALWAYS A QUICK READ.

I'VE BEEN READING THE GRAPHIC ADAPTATION OF **THE 9/11 REPORT** FOR MY CLASS.

DO YOU HAVE TO ANALYZE THE **WORDS** OR THE **IMAGES** OR **BOTH**?

THAT'S THE TRICKY PART, LUIS. ANALYZING **IMAGES** IS TOUGHER THAN I THOUGHT. BUT I FEEL PRETTY CONFIDENT TALKING ABOUT THE **WRITTEN** TEXT.

AFTER ALL, THE INFORMATION COMES STRAIGHT FROM THE **ACTUAL REPORT** OF THE 9/11 COMMISSION.

SOME OF THE LANGUAGE IS EVEN THE SAME, **WORD-FOR-WORD**, LIKE THE TITLES OF THE CHAPTERS.

graphic novel adaptation

original report

I'M THINKING OF COMPARING THE TWO SOURCES IN MY ESSAY.

EVEN BEFORE THEY TURNED IT INTO A COMIC, PARTS OF THE ORIGINAL REPORT READ MORE LIKE A **THRILLER** THAN A DRY LEGAL DOCUMENT.

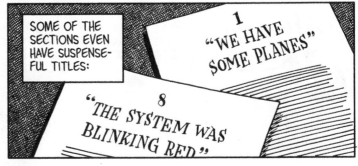

SOME OF THE SECTIONS EVEN HAVE SUSPENSE-FUL TITLES:

1
"WE HAVE SOME PLANES"

8
"THE SYSTEM WAS BLINKING RED"

I GUESS THE WRITERS OF THE **GOVERNMENT REPORT** REALLY WANTED TO GRAB PEOPLE'S ATTENTION BY DRAMATICALLY SETTING THE **SCENE**.

YEAH, THE **ORIGINAL REPORT** BEGINS WITH A DESCRIPTIVE OPENING...

THE 9/11

"TUESDAY, SEPTEMBER 11, 2001, dawned temperate and nearly cloudless in the eastern United States."

"Millions of men and women readied themselves for work."

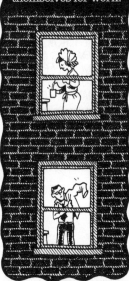

"Some made their way to the Twin Towers, the signature structures of the World Trade Center complex in New York City."

"Others went to Arlington, Virginia, to the Pentagon."

"Across the Potomac River, the United States Congress was back in session."

"At the other end of Pennsylvania Avenue, people began to line up for a White House Tour."

"In Sarasota, Florida, President George W. Bush went for an early morning run."

THAT'S A LOT LIKE THE SECTION I JUST READ ABOUT "STRATEGIC READING." FREDERICK DOUGLASS ALSO USED VERBAL PICTURES TO MAKE HIS ARGUMENT MORE ENGAGING AND CONVINCING.

BUT READING CRITICALLY MEANS MORE THAN JUST IMAGINING YOURSELF IN THE SCENE.

YOU HAVE TO ANALYZE THE CHOICE OF INDIVIDUAL ELEMENTS IN THE TEXT AND HOW THEY FIT TOGETHER IN WAYS THAT MIGHT NOT BE IMMEDIATELY OBVIOUS.

THAT SOUNDS LIKE MUCH LESS OF A THRILLER.

WELL, THERE'S STILL SOMETHING SATISFYING ABOUT ASSEMBLING ALL THOSE CLUES. I MEAN, LOOK BACK AT THAT OPENING.

THE FIRST SENTENCE IS UP IN THE CLOUDLESS SKY.

BUT THE SECOND TAKES PLACE DOWN ON THE GROUND AT THE HUMAN LEVEL.

"TUESDAY, SEPTEMBER 11, 2001, dawned temperate and nearly cloudless in the eastern United States."

"Some made their way to the Twin Towers, the signature structures of the World Trade Center complex in New York City."

"Across the Potomac River, the United States Congress was back in session."

"At the other end of Pennsylvania Avenue, people began to line up for a White House Tour."

"In Sarasota, Florida, President George W. Bush went for an early morning run."

THE THIRD SENTENCE IS ABOUT THE PRIVATE SECTOR, AND THE FOURTH IS ABOUT THE MILITARY, ALTHOUGH THEY BOTH DISCUSS DAILY COMMUTERS ON THE MOVE.

AND THE REST OF THE OPENING IS ABOUT THE PEOPLE WHO MIGHT BE ULTIMATELY RESPONSIBLE FOR PREVENTING ANOTHER TERRORIST ATTACK: THE LEGISLATIVE AND EXECUTIVE BRANCHES OF GOVERNMENT.

"BEFORE 8 O'CLOCK ON TUESDAY, SEPTEMBER 11, 2001, A PLEASANT AND CLOUDLESS MORNING IN BOSTON, TWO PLANES, BOTH BOEING 767S, WERE ABOUT TO TAKE OFF FROM LOGAN AIRPORT."

IN THE **GRAPHIC NOVEL**, THE FIRST SENTENCE FOCUSES DIRECTLY ON THE PLANES.

SO WHEN YOU LOOK CLOSELY AT THE **LANGUAGE** AND THE **LOGIC** OF A PASSAGE, YOU CAN ACTUALLY SEE **IMPLICIT ARGUMENTS** THERE.

RIGHT. BUT YOU HAVE TO **EXPLICATE** THEM.

OR **UNFOLD** THEM.

UNFOLD

READING THE **WORDS** IS EASY. I DON'T KNOW WHAT TO SAY ABOUT READING THE **PICTURES**.

?

KNOCK KNOCK!

UH...

...LUIS, I'LL HAVE TO CALL YOU BACK.

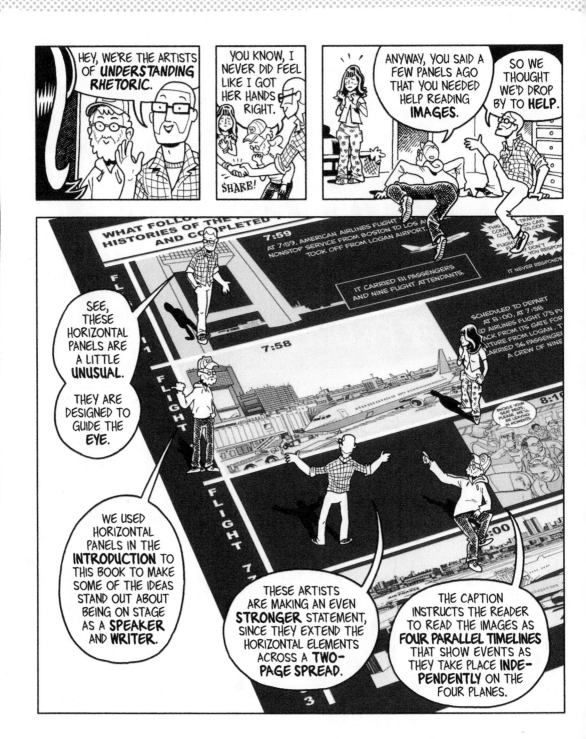

WHAT'S INTERESTING IS HOW MUCH **BLACK** THE COMIC INCLUDES.

THEY EMPHASIZE THE SERIOUS, SOBER QUALITY OF THE EVENT BY USING THE COLOR BLACK, A COLOR TRADITIONALLY ASSOCIATED WITH **MOURNING** IN OUR COUNTRY.

WE'RE FINALLY OFF, LADIES AND GENTLEMEN.

BLACK ALSO FOCUSES THE READER'S ATTENTION ON HOW MANY THINGS THAT HAPPENED IN THE HIJACKINGS ARE STILL **UNKNOWN**, BECAUSE INVESTIGATORS ARE STILL "IN THE DARK" ABOUT EXACTLY WHAT TOOK **PLACE**.

THANKS FOR THE **TIPS!**

Beep Beep Beep

HEY, LUIS, I HAVE SOME- THING TO **SHOW** YOU...

...AND THEN I HAVE TO GET BACK TO **READING**.

COMING UP IN THE NEXT EXCITING EPISODE OF **REFRAME**

"Am I having an IDENTITY CRISIS?"

[pg. 141]

1 why READ CLOSELY?

CLOSE READING ISN'T JUST FOR LITERARY TEXTS. DOCUMENTS YOU ENCOUNTER IN SCHOOL, PROFESSIONAL, AND PRIVATE LIFE ALSO CALL FOR CLOSE READING.

LOOK AT THIS DOCUMENT ABOUT POLICIES FOR MONITORING COMPUTER USE, WHICH COMES FROM A COLLEGE WEB SITE.

Under normal circumstances, college officials will not examine personal information transmitted over the network or stored on college-owned computers. However, the college reserves the right to monitor system resources, including activity and accounts, with or without notice, when:

1 It is necessary to protect the integrity, security, or functionality of college computing resources.

2 An account or system is engaged in unusual or excessive activity.

3 It has good cause to believe that regulations, rules, or laws are being violated.

4 In the event of health, safety, or security emergencies, as determined by authorized college officials.

Additionally, the normal operation and maintenance of the college's computing resources requires the backup of data, the logging of activity, the monitoring of general usage patterns, and other such activities as may be necessary in order to provide desired services.

DRAWING CONCLUSIONS

The activities below ask you to focus on the rhetorical
dimensions of texts and visuals you might write about.

1
Choose one print text and one nonprint
text that you are currently reading.
Consider all of the ways you "notate"
what you read, either in writing or
in your head. Do you make real notes?
Use stickies? Use digital stickies? If you
primarily use "mental stickies," what kinds of
questions do you ask about what you read?

Write down some questions you might ask,
or notes you might make, about the texts
you have chosen.

2
Consider how you might use some terms from
Chapter 1 -- *logos*, *ethos*, *pathos*, and *kairos* --
to engage in active reading. Pick a work you
are reading for a class and make a note of the
following: the subject, how the text builds logos,
how the writer establishes ethos, how the text
demonstrates a use of pathos, and how the writer
shows an awareness of kairos.

What do you discover? How might attending to
these rhetorical dimensions improve your ability
to read -- and summarize -- a text?

3 Choose a text that you might be called upon to analyze, such as a journal article, a work of art, or a video or film. Make a list of all of the questions you have about it, as well as all of the points that you find interesting.

Next, make a list of quotations, still images, characteristics of the work, or other information that has popped out at you during your reading of the text.

Now group these pieces according to criteria that make sense to you, as Liz does with the images from Frederick Douglass's autobiography on pp. 91-93. Consider the questions you listed in light of your arrangement of pieces from the text. Rearrange questions and textual evidence as needed. What new insights emerge for you from this process?

4 Think about the book you're reading right now -- *Understanding Rhetoric.* Look back at the discussion on pp. 87-88 of Frederick Douglass's interest in controlling the way he appeared in images in print. Why do you think that this book uses Douglass as an example? What evidence do you find that indicates that the writers and illustrators of this book thought carefully about the images it includes? What choices might you have made differently?

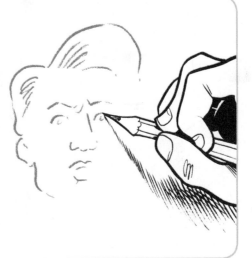

ISSUE 3

WRITING IDENTITIES

CLASS 10641
INTERN
METAMORPH

In this issue...

RHETORIC IS ABOUT PRESENTING A CHARACTER THAT AN AUDIENCE WILL **TRUST**....

... AND ABOUT BOTH INSPIRING **PASSIONATE EMOTIONS** AND STRUCTURING **RATIONAL ARGUMENTS**.

RHETORIC IS ALSO ABOUT SAYING THE RIGHT THING AT THE RIGHT TIME.

UH... L-LIZ?

IT'S, UH... UM.

YIKES!

WHAT WAS **THAT**?

AAH!

LOOOOM!!

PHONE

123

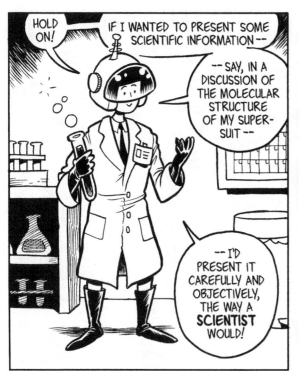

HOLD ON!

IF I WANTED TO PRESENT SOME SCIENTIFIC INFORMATION --

-- SAY, IN A DISCUSSION OF THE MOLECULAR STRUCTURE OF MY SUPER-SUIT --

-- I'D PRESENT IT CAREFULLY AND OBJECTIVELY, THE WAY A **SCIENTIST** WOULD!

BUT IF WE PUT ON OTHER COSTUMES, IT DOESN'T REALLY CHANGE WHO WE ARE.

PUTTING ON A KNIGHT'S COSTUME DOESN'T MAKE ME HEROIC.

...

NO, BUT SOCIAL CONTEXTS MATTER, AND MOST PEOPLE WEAR A LOT OF DIFFERENT COSTUMES FOR THEIR DIFFERENT SOCIAL ROLES.

CHANGING YOUR IDENTITY MAY BE ABOUT CHOOSING THE RIGHT FRAME OF MIND.

OH, I GET IT.

THIS IS AN OUTFIT I **TEACH** IN.

I DON'T REALLY WEAR IT AROUND THE **HOUSE**.

STANDING UP IN FRONT OF A CLASS SOUNDS PRETTY HEROIC TO **ME**.

A LOT OF PEOPLE TREAT PROFESSIONAL CLOTHING AS A KIND OF **ARMOR**.

IT GIVES THEM **AUTHORITY** AND MAKES THEM FEEL LESS **VULNERABLE**.

LIKEWISE, T-SHIRTS OFTEN MAKE CLEAR **RHETORICAL STATEMENTS**.

RUSTLE RUSTLE

FOR EXAMPLE, WEARING A T-SHIRT FROM A *STAR TREK* CONVENTION MIGHT SHOW THAT SOMEONE IS A BIG FAN.

LIVE LONG & PROSPER

THIS ONE IS FROM A VIDEO-GAME CONFERENCE, WHERE I GAVE A TALK ABOUT EDUCATIONAL GAMES.

GDC

SO ONE T-SHIRT IS ABOUT EXPRESSING YOUR ROLE AS A FAN, AND THE OTHER IS ABOUT YOUR ROLE AS AN ESTABLISHED EXPERT.

HERE'S A DRESS THAT I WORE WHEN I WAS A SUNDAY SCHOOL TEACHER.

MY STUDENTS EXPECTED ME TO BE FORMAL AND RESPECTABLE.

AND HERE ARE EXERCISE CLOTHES THAT I WEAR TO GYM CLASS WHEN I KNOW NOBODY'S LOOKING AT ME.

SOUNDS LIKE YOU HAVE A LOT OF DIFFERENT SOCIAL ROLES.

IN SOME ROLES YOU'RE A TEACHER, AND IN SOME YOU'RE A STUDENT.

SO YOU ALSO HAVE DIFFERENT LEVELS OF AUTHORITY.

127

TRYING OUT CHOICES FOR DIFFERENT AUDIENCES

I HOPE TO BECOME A HARDWORKING SUPERHERO, BUT SINCE I'M A RECENT COLLEGE GRADUATE, I COULD ONLY GET SUPERCON TO TAKE ME ON AS AN **UNPAID INTERN.**

IT'S TIME TO USE MY SUPERHERO POWERS OF **DISCOURSE** TO SAVE THE DAY!

ALL THE OTHER SUPERHERO INTERNS HAVE BEEN TALKING ABOUT HOW TO HANDLE THE SITUATION -- BUT THEIR TONE NEEDS SOME WORK.

HERE'S A VIDEO FROM OUR LAST SECRET MEETING....

DOOP.

PLAY

SUPERCONGLOMERATE'S TREATMENT OF SUPERHERO INTERNS IS REPREHENSIBLE.

SUPERCON'S BIGWIGS ARE TREATING US LIKE SLAVES!

133

ALL OF US SUPERHEROES PERFORM COMPLEX TASKS -- DRAWING ON WHAT WE LEARNED IN COLLEGE.

BUT EVERY JOB REQUIRES THE LEARNING OF NEW SKILLS. AN INTERNSHIP CAN BE AN IMPORTANT BRIDGE BETWEEN COLLEGE AND CAREER.

IS IT FAIR, THOUGH, TO REQUIRE ON-THE-JOB TRAINING WITHOUT COMPENSATION?

YOUR **TONE** SHOULD ENGAGE YOUR AUDIENCE IN A WAY THAT WILL INVITE THEM TO FEEL RECEPTIVE TO YOUR MESSAGE.

AND YOUR **VOICE** -- YOUR IDENTITY AS A WRITER -- SHOULD PROJECT THE APPROPRIATE KIND OF AUTHORITY AND AGENCY.

RECORDING BOOTH

EXACTLY!

I ALWAYS NEED TO THINK ABOUT THE AUDIENCE I'M TRYING TO REACH IN MY RHETORICAL SITUATION -- AND MAKE SURE I ADJUST MY TONE AND VOICE TO GET THE EFFECT I WANT.

135

AHEM.

"INCLUDING SUPERHERO INTERNS IN THE SUPERCON COMPENSATION PLAN IS THE RIGHT THING TO DO. TREATING INTERNS AS PROFESSIONAL WORKERS WILL IMPROVE CUSTOMER SERVICE AND ATTRACT BETTER TALENT TO THE FIELD."

UM, METAMORPH -- THAT WOULD BE GREAT, EXCEPT FOR ONE THING.

YES.

ACCORDING TO THIS SCHEDULE, YOU ARE SUPPOSED TO BE RECORDING A PODCAST FOR HIGH SCHOOL STUDENTS CONSIDERING A VOCATIONAL TRACK IN SUPERHERODOM.

OOPS.

I MUST HAVE MIXED UP MY NOTES.

THE IDENTITY YOU PROJECT NEEDS TO CONVEY YOUR **ETHOS**, YOUR SENSE OF **CREDIBILITY**, FOR THE AUDIENCE YOU'RE ADDRESSING.

SO LET'S TRY THAT ONE AGAIN.

"BEING A SUPER-HERO INTERN MEANS YOU GET TO PLAY WITH A LOT OF

AWESOME GEAR!

BUT CHECK OUT WHAT FORMER INTERNS HAVE SAID ABOUT SUPERCONGLOMERATE ON SOCIAL MEDIA TO SEE IF YOU'LL GET ENOUGH OUT OF YOUR INTERNSHIP TO JUSTIFY WEEKS OF WORK WITHOUT PAY..."

THAT'S BETTER!

YOU'RE DEMONSTRATING AN **ETHOS** THAT THIS AUDIENCE CAN APPRECIATE.

WHEN YOU TRIED SPECIFI-CALLY TO REACH A YOUNGER AUDIENCE, YOU CREATED A COMPLETELY **DIFFERENT** RHETORICAL EFFECT.

WELL, I **DO** HAVE SUPERPOWERS OF DISCOURSE.

THAT'S TRUE -- BUT USING DIFFERENT VOICES IN THAT WAY IS A SKILL THAT ANYONE CAN LEARN WITH ENOUGH PRACTICE.

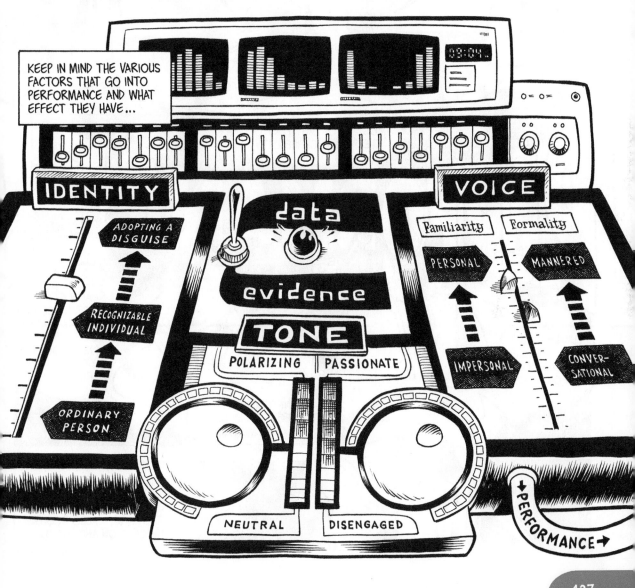

KEEP IN MIND THE VARIOUS FACTORS THAT GO INTO PERFORMANCE AND WHAT EFFECT THEY HAVE...

IDENTITY

ADOPTING A DISGUISE

RECOGNIZABLE INDIVIDUAL

ORDINARY PERSON

data

evidence

TONE

POLARIZING   PASSIONATE

NEUTRAL   DISENGAGED

VOICE

Familiarity   Formality

PERSONAL   MANNERED

IMPERSONAL   CONVER-SATIONAL

PERFORMANCE ➔

REFRAME with Luis & Cindy

Am I having an IDENTITY CRISIS?

SNAP!!

UGH.

LIBRARY STUDY ROOM

SNAP!

UGH!

CINDY?

CINDY, WHAT'S UP?

LUIS, **HELP!** I'M HAVING AN **IDENTITY CRISIS.**

I'M SUPPOSED TO WRITE AN **ETHNOGRAPHY.** BUT I'M NOT REALLY SURE WHAT THAT IS.

UGH.

WHY DID I PRETEND TO UNDERSTAND THE ASSIGNMENT?

HMM... ASKING QUESTIONS MIGHT NOT BE PART OF YOUR IDENTITY.

I'D SUGGEST A **PERSONALITY TRANSPLANT.**

VERY FUNNY. HOW ABOUT GIVING ME SOME **HELP?**

HERE, LET ME SHOW YOU THE ASSIGNMENT.

FLIP OPEN

ASSIGNMENT

One of your goals for this class is to observe and understand the complexities and nuances of online communities. In preparation for your final digital ethnography project, you'll select an online community to which you currently belong and that you can closely observe and interact with for several weeks. Participating with the group will be part of how you will understand its norms.

I'M ONLINE EVERY DAY --

SMILE!

SNAP!

I CHECK SOCIAL NETWORK SITES, BROWSE PROFILES, PARTICIPATE IN DISCUSSIONS...

TYPE TYPE

...BUT I'VE NEVER WRITTEN AN **ETHNO-GRAPHY** BEFORE!

UPLOAD...

HMM...

WELL, "ETHNO" MEANS A GROUP OF PEOPLE, AND "GRAPH" MEANS WRITING.

SO "ETHNOGRAPHY" IS JUST **WRITING ABOUT PEOPLE.**

I THINK IT'S MORE COMPLICATED THAN THAT, LUIS.

WE'RE STUDYING **ONLINE COMMUNITIES.** WE'RE SUPPOSED TO FOCUS ON GROUPS OF PEOPLE WITH **COMMON INTERESTS** WHO USE THE INTERNET AS THEIR **MAIN** METHOD OF COMMUNICATION.

AN ONLINE COMMUNITY FOSTERS IDENTIFICATION WITH A GROUP OF PEOPLE WITH SIMILAR INTERESTS OR OBJECTIVES.

MEMBERS SHARE A COMMITMENT TO VALUES HELD IN COMMON AND OFTEN SHARE LABOR AND LEADERSHIP.

COOL, I HAVE THAT ASSIGNMENT, TOO. MY PROFESSOR SAYS WE'RE SUPPOSED TO OBSERVE A GROUP AND WRITE DOWN EVERYTHING WE SEE AND HEAR.

WE'RE EXPLORING OUR IDENTITIES AS RESEARCHERS.

I DECIDED TO WRITE ABOUT VIDEO GAMES AND THE FRIENDS I'VE MADE ONLINE. GAMING HAS BEEN PART OF MY DAILY LIFE SINCE HIGH SCHOOL. IT'S A WAY TO KEEP IN TOUCH WITH OLD FRIENDS...

...AND IT HELPS ME MEET NEW PEOPLE, TOO.

IDENTITY

OF COURSE, WHEN YOU ARE WRITING ABOUT FRIENDS THAT YOU CARE ABOUT...

ADOPTING DISGUISE

RECOGNIZABLE INDIVIDUAL

...IT'S IMPORTANT TO BE **YOURSELF** AND PRESENT YOUR EXPERTISE **HONESTLY.**

ORDINARY PERSON

JUST AS YOU TELL THE TRUTH ABOUT THE SUBJECTS YOU OBSERVE.

REPORT YOUR OBSERVATIONS.

COMING UP IN THE NEXT EXCITING EPISODE OF **REFRAME**

"The OFFICE hour!"

[pg 181]

"IDENTITIES"

WALK the TALK

1 Who is the WRITER HERE?

> READERS FORM AN IMPRESSION OF YOU FROM THE IDENTITIES YOU PROJECT IN WRITING. THINK ABOUT HOW YOU CAN PRESENT YOURSELF MOST EFFECTIVELY.

> A LINKEDIN PAGE SHOWCASES A WRITER'S IDENTITY AS A PROFESSIONAL, SO YOUR GOAL ON LINKEDIN IS TO PROJECT YOUR BEST SELF FOR THE KIND OF WORK YOU WANT TO DO.

in | Search for people, jobs, companies, and more... | 🔍

Background

 Summary

My name is Uzair Mohammad, and I'm seeking to apply my engineering experience to develop and create novel devices and tools, and to build a career with an organization seeking experience in engineering design, project management, enthusiastic leadership, excellent communication, and creativity in problem solving.

-Bioengineer with 5+ years of project management experience in bioengineering and biotechnology
-Driven team leader, founder of engineering startup with novel "Biofiltration" microfilter technology
-Practiced communicator, presented TED Talk on "Biofiltration" Technology (TEDxUCSD 2014)
-Experienced with legal scientific notebooks, and science/engineering report writing, grants, and patents.
-Recognized and Awarded by US Air Force, US Navy, Lawrence Livermore National Labs, IEEE, The National Science Foundation, and Brown University for excellence in Engineering and Communication.

Courtesy Uzair Mohammad

DRAWING CONCLUSIONS

The following assignments ask you to think about
the importance of identity when composing.

1 This chapter mentions Barbara Ehrenreich's
Nickel and Dimed, a book about the struggles
of the working poor that relies on the author's
experience of getting by on minimum-wage jobs.

What personal experiences have you had that
connect you to an idea or a subject that interests
you? How can you use your experiences to explore
that subject in a piece of writing? Draft a proposal
for a writing project in a genre of your choosing
(perhaps a Web essay or a newspaper editorial)
that uses your firsthand experience to enhance
the discussion of your topic.

2 Keep notes for a week about how you
interact with others through various
online sites. How do you represent
yourself -- in filling out required or
requested information, in uploading
content, and in interacting with others?

Write a short autoethnography -- a brief
narrative describing your own use of the
sites -- that analyzes your experiences
and discusses how you use different
identities in different rhetorical situations.

3 Look at pp. 133-35 of this chapter, in which extreme and bland tones are represented both verbally and visually. Choose a short text, such as an email or online posting, that you have written in the past month with a particular audience in mind.

Who is the audience? What tone do you take in your writing? Turn your original text into an audience-appropriate media text (perhaps a comic, collage, poster, or video) that uses visuals or other nonverbal means to help convey tone.

4 Many students feel anxiety about public speaking and presenting their ideas in front of large groups of people. What is the largest audience that you have ever had to address? How did you prepare for your presentation?

Looking back, what worked well, and what should you have done differently? How did the composition of the audience affect how you felt about your performance?

ARGUMENT
BEYOND PRO AND CON

In this issue...

157

JUST LIKE IN THE ERA OF CLASSICAL RHETORIC, SPEAKERS ARE ALWAYS POINTING OUT HOW CIRCUMSTANCES **HAVE** CHANGED...

...**ARE** CHANGING...

...OR ARE **LIKELY** TO CHANGE.

AND THESE CHANGES MIGHT BE FOR THE WORSE OR FOR THE **BETTER**...

...AND THEY MIGHT BE GRADUAL "EVOLUTIONS" OR DRAMATIC "REVOLUTIONS"!

EXCUSE ME!

HEY, IF YOU REALLY WANT TO TALK ABOUT ARGUMENT, MAYBE YOU NEED A **TALK SHOW HOST!**

WHO INVITED **YOU** HERE?

THIS IS A PRIVATE CONVERSATION!

THIS DOESN'T LOOK LIKE A VERY **PRIVATE** CONVERSATION TO **ME.**

UH... RIGHT.

I GUESS WE **ARE** CHARACTERS IN A **BOOK.**

OKAY THEN...

K·CHONK!

A GOOD **ARGUMENT** IS ACTUALLY A LOT LIKE A GOOD **CONVERSATION.**

IT'S IMPORTANT TO REPRESENT **MORE** THAN ONE SIDE.

WHA--!

HUH?

GOOD POINT! IN A WAY, TALK SHOWS STAGE DEBATES AS CONVERSATIONS AMONG SEVERAL DIFFERENT PARTICIPANTS.

WHEW! GUESTS ON TALK SHOWS SOMETIMES INSIST THAT ONLY **THEIR** SIDE CAN BE RIGHT, AND THE OTHER SIDE IS NECESSARILY **WRONG**, AND THEY NEVER CONCEDE **ANYTHING** TO THEIR OPPONENTS.

CON

PLEASE, MA'AM -- A GOOD ARGUMENT HAS TO GET BEYOND PRO AND CON DEBATES BETWEEN OVERSIMPLIFIED **OPPOSITES**!

RRGH! SIR!

COMPLEX CONVERSATIONS AREN'T JUST ABOUT **RIGHT** AND **WRONG**!

KICK!

POINT ACCUSINGLY!

No! No!! YES! PRO

IN THE DEBATE ABOUT **IMMIGRATION**, FOR INSTANCE, PARTICIPANTS ARE ACTUALLY ARGUING ABOUT THEIR VALUES AND THE DIFFERENT VISIONS THEY HAVE FOR THE COUNTRY.

VIEWED THAT WAY, THE DEBATE ABOUT IMMIGRATION ISN'T JUST ABOUT WHETHER TO LET IMMIGRANTS IN OR NOT. IT'S ALSO ABOUT HOW WE WANT TO DEFINE WHAT AMERICA IS.

MAYFLOWER

NO NO O

CON

KICK 'em ouT!

YES PRO LET

THINKING ABOUT WHAT'S REALLY AT STAKE IN ANY GIVEN DEBATE REVEALS THE ARGUMENT'S **ASSERTIONS**, OR THE PARTICULAR CLAIMS BEING MADE.

A STATEMENT IS **ARGUABLE** IF IT REPRESENTS A POSITION WITH WHICH A REASON-ABLE PERSON COULD DISAGREE.

FOR INSTANCE, CONSIDER CHILDREN BROUGHT TO THIS COUNTRY **ILLEGALLY** BY THEIR PARENTS WHEN THEY WERE TOO YOUNG TO GIVE **CONSENT**.

BEFORE **AFTER**

SHOULD SUCH CHILDREN BE TREATED AS **"CRIMINALS"**? SHOULD THEY, FOR EXAMPLE, BE DENIED THE RIGHT TO ATTEND AMERICAN UNIVERSITIES?

LET'S CONSIDER THE EVIDENCE IN A LESS COMPLEX CASE.

IT LOOKS LIKE A BREAK-IN...

...BUT WAS IT?

BREAKING INTO A CABIN THAT DOESN'T BELONG TO YOU MIGHT NOT BE THE WRONG THING TO DO...

...IF YOU'RE IN AN EMERGENCY SITUATION...

...AND **IF** THE BREAK-IN COULD PREVENT SOMETHING WORSE FROM HAPPENING.

A LOT DEPENDS ON WHAT HAPPENED BEFORE THE BREAK-IN AND ON WHAT HAPPENED AFTERWARD.

HOME SWEET HOME

Papa B. Mama B. Baby B.

AND A LOT DEPENDS ON WHO IS LOOKING AT THE INCIDENT.

THE OWNER OF THIS CABIN AND THE PERSON WHO BREAKS IN MIGHT SEE THE SITUATION VERY DIFFERENTLY.

161

AN ARGUMENT NEEDS **GROUNDS** OR **EVIDENCE** FROM WHICH WE DEVELOP A POSITION.

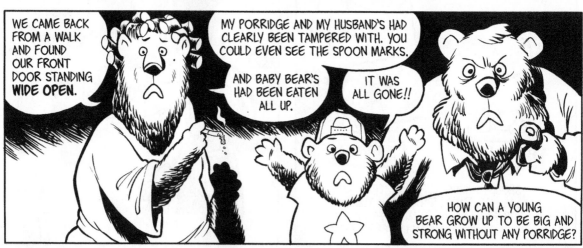

WE CAME BACK FROM A WALK AND FOUND OUR FRONT DOOR STANDING **WIDE OPEN.**

MY PORRIDGE AND MY HUSBAND'S HAD CLEARLY BEEN TAMPERED WITH. YOU COULD EVEN SEE THE SPOON MARKS.

AND BABY BEAR'S HAD BEEN EATEN ALL UP.

IT WAS ALL GONE!!

HOW CAN A YOUNG BEAR GROW UP TO BE BIG AND STRONG WITHOUT ANY PORRIDGE?

HERE'S THE BEGINNING OF AN ARGUMENT BASED ON **EVIDENCE** --

-- THE BEARS ARE EXPLAINING:

1 **WHAT** happened,

2 **HOW** it happened,

3 **WHO** was affected, and

4 **WHY** it's a problem.

EMBEDDED IN ALL OF THOSE "QUESTION WORDS" IS A COMPLEX SET OF:

WHAT Facts
HOW Circumstances
WHO Relationships
WHY Reasons

...THESE CAN BE CRITICAL PARTS OF GOOD ARGUMENTS BASED ON EVIDENCE.

NOW -- WHAT IN THE **WORLD**?

POLICE

Issue 4 • Argument Beyond Pro and Con

Y'KNOW, THEY WERE PROBABLY GOING TO HAVE A **CHEESE PLATE** OR SOMETHING IN THE JURY ROOM...

GIVE IT A **REST**, WILL YOU?

WHEN YOU TRY TO MAKE A PERSUASIVE ARGUMENT FOR COLLEGE OR FOR WORK, YOU MIGHT NOT USE THE KINDS OF CLAIMS AND EVIDENCE THAT A LAWYER WOULD CHOOSE.

YOU'LL NEED TO THINK ABOUT WHAT EVIDENCE WILL WORK IN THE CONTEXT OF **YOUR** ARGUMENT...

...AND HOW YOU CAN ORGANIZE AND PRESENT YOUR ARGUMENT MOST EFFECTIVELY.

IN CLASSROOMS AS IN COURTROOMS, ARGUMENTS ARE BUILT FROM THE GROUND UP --

EVIDENCE IS GATHERED, AND THEN LARGER CONCLUSIONS MAY BE DRAWN FROM IT.

SOMETIMES PRELIMINARY ARGUMENTS NEED TO BE REVISED...

CONCL-USIONS

EXTRAP-OLATION

EXAM-PLE

EXAM-PLE

ANALYSIS

EVIDENCE

BASE CLAIMS

GASP!

...AS...MORE EVIDENCE IS GATHERED...

NOW WE'RE TALKING, LIZ!

ACADEMIC ARGUMENTS ARE MADE UP OF **PARAGRAPHS**. AND EVERY PARAGRAPH OF AN ARGUMENT NEEDS CERTAIN PARTS TO WORK AS A COHERENT UNIT.

IT'S LIKE THIS **SANDWICH**: YOU NEED MANY DIFFERENT COMPONENTS TO MAKE A PARAGRAPH **WHOLE**.

RIGHT -- EACH PARAGRAPH IS LIKE A MINI-ARGUMENT.

NO ONE WANTS AN ARGUMENT WITHOUT...

EVIDENCE --

SLICE!

ANALYSIS --

CHOP!

IMPLICATIONS --

DICE!

-- OR CONTEXT!

HALVE!

169

Issue 4 • Argument Beyond Pro and Con

The increasing generational differences between immigrants from Japan, the Issei, and the American-born second generation, the Nisei, had divided Japanese Americans even prior to the outbreak of World War II, and this division grew more apparent in the camps in which many Japanese Americans were interned during the war years. Nisei Gene Sogioka noted during his internment, "It's not just the age gap....There are two different cultures in the camp: the Nisei, and the Issei" (qtd. in Gesensway 153). The disparity between ancient Japan and modernized America was embodied and displayed by the contrasting values, ideologies, and lifestyles of the Issei and Nisei. The Issei often insisted that Japanese be spoken throughout the camp; the Nisei, however, symbolized the idealistic quest for the "American Dream" and willingly conformed to U.S. customs (Dusselier 195). The camp structure intensified the estrangement between Issei parents and their Nisei children because the young people were no longer economically dependent on their parents; by taking away any rights to income or social status, the U.S. government had usurped the position of primary caregiver, and the structure of the Japanese American family unit neared disintegration (Ziegler 136; Dusselier 194). Due to the inability of each group to understand or accept the other's behaviors, an antagonistic relationship developed. Ted Matsuda, interned at Jerome, Arkansas, describes in his evacuation diary the frequent problems with stealing occurring in the camp (21). In his June 15 entry, he bitterly recounts, "Issei are quick to blame every fault on the Nisei" (21). Through the disunion between the Issei and Nisei, the cultural identification term "Japanese American" became fragmented by the opposing sides of its two competing ethnicities.

Adaptation of Marissa Osato essay, "Art in the Internment Camps: Designing the Japanese American Identity." Courtesy Marissa Osato.

JUST AS A SATISFYING MEAL IS COMPOSED OF MANY PROPERLY PREPARED DISHES...

...AN ENTIRE ARGUMENT ESSAY IS COMPOSED OF PROPERLY CONSTRUCTED **PARAGRAPHS**.

SO-- --LET'S TALK ABOUT HOW THE PARTS OF AN ARGUMENT WORK AS A WHOLE.

B-BUT-- BUT MY SANDWICH--

WELCOME BACK!

YOU'RE JUST IN TIME FOR THE NEXT QUESTION!

PRO & CON

WHEN I WAS IN HIGH SCHOOL, THEY TAUGHT US TO WRITE **FIVE-PARAGRAPH ESSAYS:**

AN **INTRODUCTION.**

THREE EXAMPLES TO PROVE THE POINT.

AND A **CONCLUSION** THAT RESTATES THE INTRODUCTION.

WELL, MOST WRITING YOU DO AFTER HIGH SCHOOL WON'T FOLLOW SUCH A SIMPLE FORMULA.

RIGHT-- --PEOPLE DON'T USUALLY WRITE THAT WAY WHEN THEY HAVE SOMETHING TO SAY AND AN AUDIENCE TO SAY IT TO.

ALL RIGHT -- -- THEN LET'S LOOK AT AN EXAMPLE OF THE KIND OF ARGUMENT THAT A COLLEGE INSTRUCTOR MIGHT FACE.

OKAY...

RECENTLY, JONATHAN AND I HAVE BEEN DEBATING WHETHER OR NOT GRADES SHOULD BE RELEASED TO PARENTS OF COLLEGE-AGED STUDENTS.

I AM LEANING TOWARD YES.

AND I'M LEANING TOWARD NO.

SEEMS LIKE A PRETTY STRAIGHTFORWARD DEBATE ON TODAY'S

"PRO and CON!"

ER...

...MR. HOST...

...NOT EXACTLY. I MEAN, IT MIGHT LOOK LIKE THAT ON THE SURFACE, BUT SITUATIONS ARE SELDOM SO SIMPLE.

IT'S TRUE THAT WE ARE STARTING WITH DIFFERENT ASSERTIONS...

...BUT I THINK THERE ARE STILL SOME THINGS THAT WE AGREE ON.

AND MAYBE WE'LL REACH A CONCLUSION THAT IS SOMEWHERE BETWEEN OUR TWO STARTING POSITIONS.

LET'S HEAR FROM OUR AUDIENCE.

YES, MA'AM -- YOUR QUESTION?

Issue 4 • Argument Beyond Pro and Con

IN FACT, THE LAWS CREATED BY THE FAMILY EDUCATIONAL RIGHTS AND PRIVACY ACT [FERPA] REQUIRE THAT STUDENTS WAIVE IN WRITING THEIR RIGHT TO PRIVACY IF THEY'D LIKE THEIR PARENTS TO KNOW ABOUT THEIR GRADES.

CINDY'S GRADES

SO THE **LAW** IS ACTUALLY ON THE SIDE OF STUDENTS' PRIVACY.

WE CAN ARGUE WHETHER THAT LAW IS GOOD OR NOT.

the LAW

IS IT USEFUL AND HELPFUL FOR STUDENTS' SUCCESS IN COLLEGE?

WE COULD ALSO ASK ABOUT **CAUSE AND EFFECT** -- HOW MIGHT THE FERPA GUIDELINES LEAD TO GREATER STUDENT RESPONSIBILITY?

CAUSE & EFFECT

OR **NOT**?

ARGUING ALONG THESE LINES MIGHT ALSO ALLOW US TO ADDRESS THE QUESTION OF THE VALUES REPRESENTED BY THE GUIDELINES.

VALUES

FURTHERMORE, WHILE WE SEEM TO BE STARTING FROM DIFFERENT POSITIONS IN THIS ARGUMENT...

...WE SHOULD ALSO CONSIDER WHAT BOTH POSITIONS HAVE IN COMMON.

YES!

BOTH ASSERTIONS ARE FRAMED BY THE DESIRE TO HAVE STUDENTS **SUCCEED** IN COLLEGE!

THAT'S **RIGHT!**

THESE ARE JUST TWO DIFFERENT METHODS FOR ACHIEVING THE COMMON GOAL OF STUDENT SUCCESS: ALLOWING PARENTS TO MONITOR STUDENTS FREQUENTLY...

...OR ALLOWING STUDENTS THE FREEDOM TO BECOME RESPONSIBLE FOR THEIR OWN GRADES, WITHOUT PARENTS AND GUARDIANS CONSTANTLY WATCHING OVER THEM.

BUT **WAIT**--

IF WE ARGUE THAT PARENTS SHOULD KNOW STUDENTS' GRADES...

...ARE WE ASSUMING THAT PARENTS KNOW BEST HOW TO MOTIVATE THEIR CHILDREN TO DO BETTER?

INDEED!

REPORT CARD

WE MAY BE MAKING THAT ASSUMPTION IF WE RELEASE GRADE INFORMATION.

YOU MIGHT HAVE THE START OF A GOOD COUNTER-ARGUMENT.

HMPH.

PRECISELY.

HE HAS A GOOD **POINT**.

PERHAPS THERE'S A WAY TO NEGOTIATE BETWEEN THE TWO SIDES OF THIS DEBATE.

WE MIGHT ARGUE, FOR INSTANCE, THAT STUDENTS NEED ROOM TO DEVELOP RESPONSIBILITY ON THEIR OWN...

...HOWEVER, IN SERIOUS OR SEVERE CASES, WE MIGHT RESPOND TO PARENTS' AND GUARDIANS' INQUIRIES...

...BUT ONLY IN CASES THAT MERITED SUCH AN ACTION--

UNLESS, OF COURSE, THE STUDENT HAD ALREADY WAIVED HIS OR HER RIGHT TO PRIVACY.

AAAAANNND... ...WE'RE OUT OF TIME!

WHOOSH!!

REFRAME with Luis & Cindy

The OFFICE hour!

WHAT DO YOU THINK THEY **DO** IN THERE WHEN THE DOOR IS CLOSED?

WHO KNOWS? PROBABLY READ IMPORTANT WORKS OF LITERATURE.

OR SOMETHING.

HOW DO YOU THINK THAT DOG STAYS ON THAT SKATEBOARD?

UGH! I CAN WRITE BETTER THAN THIS.

I JUST WANT IT TO BE **EASY.**

I WANT TO COME IN WITH MY WRITING AND JUST HAVE THEM **FIX** IT FOR ME.

LET ME JUST HOOK YOU UP TO OUR DIAGNOSTIC MACHINE.

WE'LL GET YOU FINISHED IN A JIFFY!

INSTEAD IT'S LIKE THEY EXPECT ME TO KNOW EVERYTHING ABOUT HOW MY ESSAY WORKS, AND THEY EXPECT ME TO FIX IT **MYSELF.**

ARE YOU SURE THAT YOU WANT TO MAKE A **BICYCLE** OUT OF THOSE PIECES?

MAYBE A TRICYCLE OR A UNICYCLE WOULD BE MORE APPROPRIATE OR GET YOU MORE ATTENTION.

I DON'T HAVE MUCH OF A DRAFT YET FOR MY RESPONSE AND COUNTERARGUMENT ASSIGNMENT.

THAT'S OKAY.

YOU CAN COME TO OFFICE HOURS JUST TO HAVE A CONVERSATION ABOUT HOW TO GET STARTED.

SO...

...I READ THE BOOK BY ANYA KAMENETZ THAT YOU ASSIGNED, ABOUT REFORMING THE U.S. COLLEGE SYSTEM...

DIY U

ME TOO!

CAN WE TALK ABOUT IT TOGETHER?

SURE!

OKAY, SO...

...WHAT DID YOU THINK OF DIY U?

TO BE HONEST, MOSTLY I AGREE WITH THE AUTHOR.

I WORRY ABOUT THE RISING COST OF EDUCATION.

AND I WORRY ABOUT THE QUALITY OF EDUCATION I'M GETTING IN COLLEGE.

ch-CHING! ch-CHING!

$138 per class hour!!

$ $ $ $ $

ch-ch ching

I USED TO THINK IT WAS ALL ABOUT GETTING GOOD GRADES, BUT NOW THAT TUITION FOR COLLEGE KEEPS GOING UP...

GRADES A

BILL $

ABSOLUTELY! STUDENTS ARE RIGHT TO WORRY ABOUT GETTING GOOD GRADES AND KEEPING THEIR PARENTS HAPPY.

BUT A LOT OF THEM ALSO CARE ABOUT THE BIG PICTURE AND THEIR FINANCIAL FUTURES.

I WISH IT WERE THAT SIMPLE!

THINK OF WHAT WE TALKED ABOUT IN CLASS.

EXPLAINING RISING TUITION RATES IS LIKE EXPLAINING WHY STUDENTS' GRADES HAVE IMPROVED.

YOU NEED TO GRAPPLE WITH CONFLICTING THEORIES.

COLLEGE IS PART OF THE "AMERICAN DREAM," SO POTENTIAL STUDENTS CREATE A HUGE DEMAND FOR HIGHER EDUCATION.

THAT DEMAND IS STOKED BY MARKETERS WHO WANT TO ATTRACT STUDENTS BY "SELLING" THE IMAGE OF CERTAIN COLLEGES TO MAKE THEIR "BRANDS" ATTRACTIVE.

THAT DEMAND IS ALSO DRIVEN UP BY LOAN POLICIES THAT MAKE A LARGE AMOUNT OF CREDIT AVAILABLE TO YOUNG BORROWERS AS LONG AS THEY USE IT FOR COLLEGE.

HIGH DEMAND DRIVES UP PRICES, ESPECIALLY WHEN SO MANY STUDENTS WANT TO GO TO A SELECTIVE FOUR-YEAR SCHOOL.

KAMENETZ ALSO SAYS THAT SUPPLY AND DEMAND IS ONLY PART OF THE STORY.

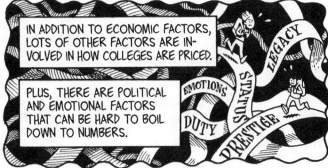

IN ADDITION TO ECONOMIC FACTORS, LOTS OF OTHER FACTORS ARE INVOLVED IN HOW COLLEGES ARE PRICED.

PLUS, THERE ARE POLITICAL AND EMOTIONAL FACTORS THAT CAN BE HARD TO BOIL DOWN TO NUMBERS.

LEGACY STATUS EMOTIONS PRESTIGE DUTY

OKAY, BUT I'M NOT SURE I GOT THAT PART ABOUT COMPARING THE COST OF HIGHER EDUCATION TO THE COST OF HEALTH CARE...

WELL, LET'S TAKE A LOOK AT THAT PASSAGE.

SHE'S USING EVIDENCE TO SUPPORT HER CLAIM. SHE QUOTES AN ECONOMIST NAMED RICK MATTOON-- TWICE!

BUT WHAT DOES **HEALTH CARE** HAVE TO DO WITH ANYTHING?

THE BIG CLAIM SHE IS PRESENTING IS HERE IN HER TOPIC SENTENCE: SUPPLY AND DEMAND CAN BE MANIPULATED BY COLLEGES.

WE HAVE TO RELY ON THE COLLEGES TO PROVIDE US WITH INFORMATION ABOUT HOW THEY WILL SPEND OUR MONEY.

WE DON'T KNOW WHY OUR COLLEGE CHARGES WHAT IT CHARGES OR WHETHER HIGHER TUITION MEANS THAT WE'LL GET A BETTER EDUCATION.

Supply and demand, for one thing, can be manipulated. "There's a system bias: this is imperfect information economics," says Rick Mattoon, an economist at the Federal Reserve Bank of Chicago and an expert on the economics of higher education. Markets function best when both buyers and sellers are well informed. When either side is missing information, prices are likely to be too low or too high. In health care, for example, comparison shopping is difficult because patients lack expertise about the relative benefits of various treatments. In the case of education too, Mattoon argues, "There's very little transparency. The schools have all the power. As an applicant you have to tell them everything about your financial situation, your ability to pay for the education, and they tell you nothing about their cost of supplying it. It's even worse than an airline," where people sitting in adjoining seats may have paid very different fares. "In higher ed everyone is paying a radically different price for the same good. . . . If you want to get suspicious about it, it's cartel behavior."

College administrators don't like being referred to as a cartel, a group that colludes to set prices. Their preferred excuse for raising tuition is their own operating costs, especially wages. . . .

I GET IT. IT'S AN **ANALOGY.** ONE DOCTOR MIGHT ORDER EXPENSIVE TESTS WHILE ANOTHER ONE MIGHT SEND YOU HOME WITH TWO ASPIRIN.

YOU HAVE TO TRUST THAT THE DOCTOR YOU PICK WILL RECOMMEND THE BEST THING FOR YOU.

AND LOOK AT THE **RHETORICAL STRATEGY** THAT KAMENETZ IS USING HERE, MAKING LIVELY COMPARISONS TO THE HEALTH CARE SYSTEM AND THEN TO THE AIRLINE INDUSTRY.

AND THE LAST SENTENCE ACTUALLY WORKS AS A TRANSITION TO THE BEGINNING OF THE FOLLOWING PARAGRAPH.

HERE, THE TOPIC SENTENCE IS ACTUALLY THE **SECOND** SENTENCE IN THE PARAGRAPH.

YOU CAN TELL FROM KAMENETZ'S CHOICE OF WORDS THAT SHE IS GOING TO ARGUE WITH THE ADMINISTRATORS.

SHE CALLS THEIR DEFENSE A "PREFERRED EXCUSE" RATHER THAN AN ARGUMENT SUPPORTED BY THE FACTS!

WOW.

THERE'S A LOT GOING ON IN THIS BOOK!

I CAN DEFINITELY SEE HOW SHE'S BUILDING HER ARGUMENT.

SPEAKING OF ARGUMENTS... CAN WE TAKE A LOOK AT MY DRAFT NOW?

COMING UP IN THE NEXT EXCITING EPISODE OF **REFRAME**

"Get it TOGETHER!"

[pg. 209]

DRAWING CONCLUSIONS

The following assignments ask you to
think about creating effective arguments.

1 Map out the financial and personal costs of your college education and the financial and personal gains you hope to get from it. Use both text and visuals to present compelling information about your college costs.

What argument do you think your map is making? Write a few paragraphs explaining how you would persuade an interested audience (such as a family member) that your studies are -- or are not -- worthwhile.

2 Choose an episode of a TV show you're very familiar with, and try to think about the kinds of "arguments" the show makes outside of its plot. (Crime dramas often argue against government bureaucracy as much as they clearly take a stance against crime.)

Once you have some thoughts on the show's arguments, think about how it goes about making those arguments: is it purely through storytelling, or do visuals and other elements play a part as well?

3 Create your own short dramatic script using a popular fable or fairy tale, and imagine how characters might interact in a courtroom setting. Try performing the scenes in small groups for your classmates.

4 Create a plan for a Web site that would discuss an issue that interests you in an engaging way. How would you show the seriousness (or lack of seriousness) of the issue to a particular audience? What evidence would you need to include on the site, and how would you present that evidence -- using links? text? images? media files? How would you organize the site?

Present your plan to a small group of classmates and collect feedback on your site proposal.

195

MULTIPLYING YOUR RESEARCH OPTIONS

RHETORIC BUILDING

SO MUCH FOR THE **PROTEST.**

YEAH, WHAT'RE WE S'POSED TO DO WITH ALL OF THESE LEFTOVER SIGNS?

YIKES!

COYOTE!

≈SLIP INSIDE!≈

SO LET'S TAKE A CLOSER LOOK AT HOW TO **MANAGE** COLLABORATIVE PROBLEM-SOLVING, AS WELL AS THE KINDS OF COLLABORATIVE WRITING YOU MIGHT BE CALLED UPON TO DO ON CAMPUS.

UM, LIZ.

SPEAKING OF PROBLEMS...

eek!!

HEY!

I WAS SAVING THAT FOR THE NEXT CHAPTER!

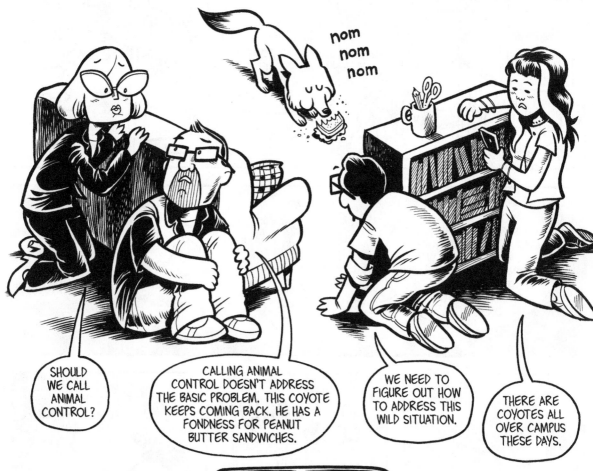

nom
nom
nom

SHOULD WE CALL ANIMAL CONTROL?

CALLING ANIMAL CONTROL DOESN'T ADDRESS THE BASIC PROBLEM. THIS COYOTE KEEPS COMING BACK. HE HAS A FONDNESS FOR PEANUT BUTTER SANDWICHES.

WE NEED TO FIGURE OUT HOW TO ADDRESS THIS WILD SITUATION.

THERE ARE COYOTES ALL OVER CAMPUS THESE DAYS.

HMM...

⚙ TakYak ®

👤 COYOTES EVERYWHERE !!
★52

👤 DRIVING ME CRAY
★16

👤 TOOK MY LUNCH :C
★5

OTHER STUDENTS ON CAMPUS HAVE REPORTED COYOTES ROAMING WALKWAYS, AND EVEN DUMPSTER-DIVING IN THE GARBAGE BINS BEHIND THE DORMS.

WE COULD ORGANIZE A PROTEST MARCH AND STORM THE GATES OF THE ADMINISTRATION BUILDING!

Yeah!

AND IF THAT DOESN'T WORK WE CAN TAKE THE LAW INTO OUR OWN HANDS!

Right on!

UM, EXCUSE ME...

EX*CUSE* ME!

OH, HEY, FLORA.

STILL ROCKIN' THE **PITH HELMET**, I SEE.

LOOK, PROTESTS AND MOBS ARE...UH, **OPTIONS**...

BUT LET'S SEE IF WE CAN COME UP WITH A BETTER PLAN.

IF WE REALLY WANT TO KEEP THESE COYOTES OFF CAMPUS...

...LET'S BEGIN BY CONSIDERING THE **CONTEXT** OF THIS SITUATION.

LITTLE HELP?

WHITE-BOARD STORAGE CLOSET

CONTEXT? WELL, LET'S SEE. I DON'T THINK COYOTES ARE **ENDANGERED** OR ANYTHING.

NO, BUT MANY COYOTES ARE ADAPTING TO SUBURBAN AND URBAN HABITATS AS DEVELOPMENT SPREADS.

WE'VE BEEN STUDYING THIS IN MY ZOOLOGY CLASS.

HEY, THIS PLACEMAT TURNED OUT GREAT!

YEAH, BUT YOU KNOW...

COYOTES ON CAMPUS
HOW WE CAN ALL HELP:

...WE'VE BEEN FOCUSING ON REACHING STUDENTS. BUT MAYBE THERE ARE OTHERS WHOSE HELP WE NEED TO SOLVE THIS PROBLEM.

LIKE INSTRUCTORS? AND STAFF?

RIGHT!

ADMINISTRATORS
STAFF
STUDENTS
INSTRUCTORS
AUDIENCE

YOU KNOW, OUR CAMPUS ADMINISTRATION NEEDS TO TAKE ACTION, TOO.

WE COULD ADDRESS THE COYOTE PROBLEM IN A PRESENTATION EXPLAINING HOW THE ADMINISTRATION CAN GET INVOLVED.

I THINK I EVEN KNOW WHAT HOOK TO USE!

IMAGINE A MAN. A MAN WHO LOST HIS LUNCH...TO A COYOTE!

gasp!

SO NOW WE'RE TACKLING THE COYOTE ISSUE ON TWO FRONTS!

PLACEMAT
△ 1
AUTHOR   STUDENTS

PRESENTATION
△ 2
AUTHOR   ADMINISTRATION

YOUR TWO TEXTS MAY BE VERY DIFFERENT BECAUSE YOU ARE APPEALING TO DIFFERENT AUDIENCES.

BUT STUDENTS AND ADMINISTRATORS WILL NEED TO WORK TOGETHER TO GET THE PROBLEM SOLVED.

SOMETIMES COLLABORATION INVOLVES COORDINATING MULTIPLE SMALLER PROJECTS TO SOLVE A LARGER PROBLEM.

207

REFRAME with Luis & Cindy

Get it TOGETHER!

HEY, GUYS, CAN WE GET TOGETHER TODAY? I NEED YOUR HELP.

AND SO...

HI, FLORA, WHAT'S UP?

CAMPUS COFFEE

HEY! LIZ ASKED US TO GET PEER FEEDBACK ON SUMMARIES OF AN ARTICLE WE HAD TO READ.

WHAT'S THE SUMMARY ABOUT?

IT'S ACTUALLY ABOUT **TEXTING**.

IT'S AN ARTICLE WITH THREE COAUTHORS. THEY PUBLISHED THEIR RESEARCH IN A JOURNAL CALLED *THE HEALTH EDUCATOR*.

SCHOLARLY RESEARCH ABOUT TEXTING? SOUNDS INTERESTING!

DOESN'T THAT SOUND INTERESTING, CINDY?

bleep-BLOOP!

...HMM?

HERE'S MY SUMMARY.

Hudson, Bliss, and Fetro talked to four groups of students to figure out how text messaging shapes how college students think about personal health. Text messaging is often linked to negative consequences such as sleep deprivation, lousy driving, and random hook-ups.But the authors wanted to gather information directly from college students rather than rely on sterotypes about kids today. The students in the four groups talked a lot about "comfort," "control," and "dependancy."When asked if they thought text messaging had a more positive or negative impact on their health, the results were confusing. They said texting allowed them to keep in touch, flirt with less awkwardness, and get better jobs, but it definitely led to more jealousy in their love lives.

COMING UP IN THE NEXT EXCITING EPISODE OF **REFRAME**

"Wrong turns or shortcuts?"

[pg 245]

DRAWING CONCLUSIONS

The following assignments ask you to practice finding,
evaluating, and responding to research sources.

1

Make an inventory of all your past experiences
with collaboration. Think broadly about when,
where, and how you have worked with other
people on any kind of project.

List all the ways in which your collective efforts
resulted in a better outcome than individual work
might have provided. What challenges did you face?
How did you resolve them? Write a short personal
guide for your peers about working collaboratively.

2

Throughout this book the characters
interact with different social media
platforms. How are such platforms
collaborative forms of knowledge building
and sharing?

In interacting socially on such platforms, have
you developed insights and ideas that you
otherwise might not have had?

Compose a blog post in which you consider
how such platforms are collaborative spaces,
and invite others to respond to your ideas.

3

Issues that could use some collaborative thinking and collective effort are all around us. Consider an issue facing your campus or neighborhood.

Begin brainstorming about the issue, and then reflect on how collaborating with others might work to address it.

Who should be involved? What kinds of thinking will you have to do together to understand and work on the issue? What kinds of tasks can be divvied up? What composing tools (e.g., collaborative authoring software) might assist your group in getting it together?

4

Cut out a rhetorical triangle to help you visualize at least two possible solutions for a specific problem on your campus.

Use one side for one approach and the flip side for the other. What media would work best to get your message out to the public?

Who is your audience, and what would motivate them to collaborate on the solution? Whom do you envision helping you on your composing team?

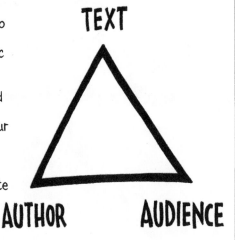

Issue 6 • Research: More Than Detective Work

Issue 6 • Research: More Than Detective Work

225

Successful DETECTION & RESEARCH tips!

START

Distinguish between PRIMARY and SECONDARY sources

RESEARCH as widely as possible

READ as much of each SOURCE as possible

EVALUATE your sources

★ LOSE A TURN! ★

SUMMARIZE or PARAPHRASE your sources-- in your OWN WORDS!

Select useful QUOTATIONS

★ ROLL AGAIN! ★

Exercise CAUTION when CUTTING and PASTING SOURCES

GO BACK TO START

Always CITE SOURCES

★ GO BACK 2 SPACES ★

A+

BUT IF YOU WRITE A TELL-ALL BOOK YEARS LATER, THAT WON'T BE A PRIMARY SOURCE ANYMORE.

RIGHT?

ACTUALLY, IF I WITNESSED OR PARTICIPATED IN AN EVENT, HISTORIANS WOULD CONSIDER MY ACCOUNT A **PRIMARY SOURCE**...

...NO MATTER WHEN THE ACCOUNT WAS WRITTEN.

EXPERIMENTAL RESULTS AND FIELD RESEARCH ARE ALSO PRIMARY SOURCES THAT OTHER RESEARCHERS CAN BUILD ON.

GOVERNMENT DOCUMENTS CAN BE IMPORTANT PRIMARY SOURCES FOR RESEARCH PROJECTS AS WELL.

A PRIMARY SOURCE DOESN'T NEED TO BE A WRITTEN TEXT, EITHER.

PAINTINGS, SOUND RECORDINGS, FILMS, BUILDINGS -- ALL OF THESE AND MORE CAN BE PRIMARY SOURCES YOU MIGHT EXPLORE IN A CLASS OR IN OTHER WRITING CONTEXTS.

BLUEPRINTS

A **SECONDARY SOURCE** IS A SOURCE THAT DESCRIBES, ANALYZES, OR INTERPRETS A PRIMARY SOURCE.

BOOKS AND ARTICLES ABOUT LITERATURE, SCIENCE, OR ART MIGHT BE CONSIDERED SECONDARY SOURCES.

2

SO IF I WROTE AN ESSAY ABOUT ARTHUR MILLER'S *THE CRUCIBLE*, WHICH WAS ABOUT THE SALEM WITCH TRIALS IN MASSACHUSETTS IN 1692...

...AND USED A SCHOLARLY ARTICLE FROM A JOURNAL OF THEATER STUDIES...

...MILLER'S PLAY WOULD BE A **PRIMARY SOURCE**, AND THE JOURNAL ARTICLE WOULD BE A **SECONDARY SOURCE**.

RIGHT!

THE ARTICLE PROVIDES AN INTERPRETATION OF MILLER'S PLAY.

WHAT'S TRICKY IS THAT A SECONDARY SOURCE IN ONE SITUATION MIGHT BE A PRIMARY SOURCE IN ANOTHER.

FOR EXAMPLE, THE SAME ARTICLE YOU'RE USING AS A SECONDARY SOURCE FOR YOUR PROJECT ON *THE CRUCIBLE* COULD BE A **PRIMARY SOURCE** FOR A RESEARCH PROJECT ON THE AUTHOR OF THE ARTICLE.

A SUBJECT LIKE THE SALEM WITCH TRIALS CAN INTEREST RESEARCHERS IN MANY FIELDS.

INDEED, SCHOLARS LOOK FOR DIFFERENT KINDS OF EVIDENCE IN APPROACHING THE SAME SUBJECT...

...AND THEY MAY EVEN DRAW DIFFERENT CONCLUSIONS FROM THE SAME EVIDENCE.

Bettmann/Getty Images

HISTORIANS WHO STUDY RACE LOOK AT HOW PERCEIVED RACIAL DIFFERENCES AND STEREOTYPES ABOUT SLAVES MIGHT HAVE PLAYED INTO THE PURITANS' HYSTERIA ABOUT WITCHES.

HOWEVER, SCHOLARS DISAGREE ABOUT THE ETHNICITIES OF THE TOWN'S RESIDENTS AND HOW RACE WAS PERCEIVED IN 1690s NEW ENGLAND.

ETHNO-HISTORY

ECONOMISTS MIGHT LOOK AT SUPPLY AND DEMAND TO UNDERSTAND THE EVENTS THAT TOOK PLACE IN SALEM VILLAGE, PARTICULARLY WHEN CROPS FAILED OR VILLAGERS SQUABBLED OVER PROPERTY RIGHTS.

SOMETIMES EVEN THE "FACTS" OF HISTORICAL CASES MAY BE OPEN TO DEBATE.

RAINFALL STATISTICS AND THE LOCATIONS OF PROPERTY LINES WEREN'T RECORDED AS CAREFULLY IN 1692 AS THEY ARE TODAY.

JOURNAL of ECONOMIC PERSPECTIVES

Bettmann/Getty Images

RYE BREAD

SOME SCHOLARS HAVE ARGUED THAT THE AFFLICTED PEOPLE OF SALEM WERE ACTUALLY HALLUCINATING AFTER EATING CONTAMINATED RYE.

YOU SHOULD CONSULT MULTIPLE SOURCES TO GET A SENSE OF THE SCHOLARLY DEBATES SURROUNDING YOUR RESEARCH TOPIC. NOT EVERYONE AGREES THAT WHAT THE PURITANS ATE WAS TO BLAME FOR THE SALEM WITCH HYSTERIA.

JOURNAL of RYE

R.Q. RYE QUARTERLY

STUDY: Rye Best for Grilled Cheese

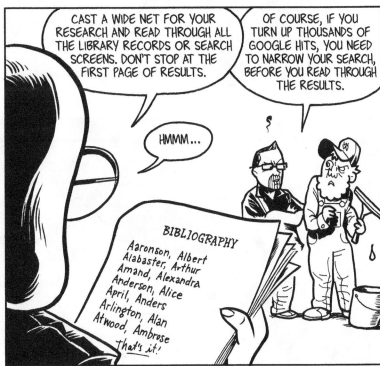

CAST A WIDE NET FOR YOUR RESEARCH AND READ THROUGH ALL THE LIBRARY RECORDS OR SEARCH SCREENS. DON'T STOP AT THE FIRST PAGE OF RESULTS.

OF COURSE, IF YOU TURN UP THOUSANDS OF GOOGLE HITS, YOU NEED TO NARROW YOUR SEARCH, BEFORE YOU READ THROUGH THE RESULTS.

HMMM...

BIBLIOGRAPHY
Aaronson, Albert
Alabaster, Arthur
Amand, Alexandra
Anderson, Alice
April, Anders
Arlington, Alan
Atwood, Ambrose
That's it!

Issue 6 • Research: More Than Detective Work

DECIDING WHICH SOURCES TO TRUST

233

Jonathan Alexander says:
HOWEVER, THERE ARE SOME SITUATIONS WHERE ONLINE SOURCES WITH A STRONG SELF-INTEREST, SUCH AS TWEETS AND STATUS UPDATES, MAY GIVE AN INSIDER'S VIEW OF CURRENT EVENTS.

@Lizlosh
THINK ABOUT WHICH SOURCES WILL BEST SERVE YOUR PURPOSE IN THIS CONTEXT.

YOU CAN ALSO LOOK FOR INFORMATION ABOUT THE CREATOR OF A POTENTIAL SOURCE.

IS THIS PERSON A SCHOLAR, AN EXPERT, OR AN INFORMED OBSERVER? HOW CAN YOU FIND OUT?

IF THE PERSON TEACHES AT A UNIVERSITY, YOU MIGHT LOOK AT HIS OR HER FACULTY WEB PAGE.

Alexander, Jonathan

Professor of English and Director of the Center for Excellence in Writing and Communication at the University of California, Irvine.

IT MIGHT GIVE YOU A BETTER SENSE OF THE SCHOLAR'S PERSONALITY, RESEARCH INTERESTS, AND DEPTH OF KNOWLEDGE ON THE SUBJECT.

A WRITER REGARDED AS AN EXPERT MAY OFTEN BE CITED BY OTHERS.

To: Luis
From: Cindy

Hey, check o[ut]
this blog abou[t]
Arthur Mille[r]
H's RAD!
http://www.arthur[...]
Later!
Cindy

REPLY   DELETE

Reference + Information

A LIBRARY'S CATALOG AND DATABASES CAN SHOW THE ACADEMIC WORK THAT A PARTICULAR AUTHOR HAS PUBLISHED.

YOU CAN USE AN INTER-NET SEARCH ENGINE TO FIND OUT ABOUT WRITERS WHO AREN'T ACADEMICS.

MANY AUTHORS HAVE PERSONAL WEB PAGES WITH INFORMATION ABOUT THEIR WORK.

CHECK A SOURCE'S DATE OF PUBLICATION.

A RECENT BOOK OR ARTICLE IS LIKELY TO CONTAIN REFERENCES TO THE MOST CURRENT RESEARCH.

DISCIPLINES SUCH AS THE SCIENCES MAY REQUIRE UP-TO-DATE SOURCES, SINCE KNOWLEDGE IN THOSE DISCIPLINES CHANGES RAPIDLY.

the BENEFITS of LEECHES 1756

IN OTHER DISCIPLINES, SUCH AS HISTORY, OLDER ACCOUNTS MIGHT SOMETIMES BE APPROPRIATE.

A WORD OF CAUTION: THINK CARE-FULLY ABOUT POPULAR PERIODICALS.

IF YOUR BEST SOURCE IS A NEWS-PAPER ARTICLE, YOU SHOULD PROBABLY KEEP LOOKING.

POPULAR NEWS
She Sings!

JOURNALISTS OFTEN HAVE GOOD GENERAL KNOWLEDGE...

...AND GOOD WRITING SKILLS...

BUT MOST REPORTERS AREN'T SPECIALISTS WITH IN-DEPTH KNOWLEDGE OF THE TOPIC.

INSTEAD, SEE IF THE NEWSPAPER ARTICLE MENTIONS A PROFESSOR, A GOVERNMENT OFFICIAL, OR ANOTHER EXPERT ON THE TOPIC, AND THEN SEARCH FOR INFORMATION FROM THESE SPECIFIC SOURCES.

ADS

SUMMARY   PARAPHRASE   QUOTATION

SETTING UP CONTEXTS AND PROVIDING BACKGROUND INFORMATION

GIVING A SENSE OF THE AUTHOR'S ARGUMENT

DRAWING ATTENTION TO SOMETHING PARTICULARLY EVOCATIVE OR INSIGHTFUL IN THE AUTHOR'S OWN WORDS

LET'S TALK ABOUT SUMMARIZING, PARAPHRASING, AND QUOTING -- HOW TO DO THEM, WHEN, AND WHY.

SUMMARIZING

PRESENTS A CONCISE, GENERAL SENSE OF WHAT YOUR SOURCE IS ABOUT.

OFTEN, SUMMARIZING GIVES A BROAD OVERVIEW OF MATERIAL THAT IS NOT IN DISPUTE.

HERE'S A SUMMARY THAT USES CONTENT FROM A WIKIPEDIA ARTICLE:

"The history of detective fiction dates back to 1841, when Edgar Allan Poe introduced Monsieur C. Auguste Dupin in the short story 'The Murders in the Rue Morgue.' Today it includes the police procedural, the legal thriller, the courtroom drama, the locked room mystery, hard-boiled fiction, the noir novel, and the 'cozy,' in which sex and violence are downplayed. In the 'cozy,' the protagonist is often a female amateur, and humor and social satire might be important parts of the narrative."

BRRT!!

I HOPE YOU PLAN TO **CITE** THAT SOURCE, SINCE YOU ARE USING SOME VERY **SPECIALIZED** KNOWLEDGE.

ABSOLUTELY.

EVEN WHEN THE WORDS ARE MINE, I HAVE TO CITE SOURCES WHEN I USE THE IDEAS OF OTHERS.

WHEN I'M SUMMARIZING MY SOURCES, I ALWAYS RECORD INFORMATION ABOUT EACH SOURCE SO I KNOW EXACTLY WHERE I FOUND IT.

BRRRT!

WOULD YOU **STOP** THAT?

SINCE WIKIPEDIA IS COLLABORATIVELY AUTHORED AND FREQUENTLY CHANGED, NOT EVERYONE CONSIDERS IT A RELIABLE SOURCE.

YES.

BUT LUCKILY, GOOD WIKIPEDIA ARTICLES OFTEN CITE AUTHORITATIVE SOURCES, SO YOU CAN CONTINUE YOUR DETECTIVE WORK THERE.

SO, IN **SUMMARY**...

=WINK=

...SUMMARIES MAY JUST RESTATE INFORMATION THE READER ALREADY KNOWS, LIKE THE GENERAL PLOT OF A NOVEL OR THE MAIN IDEAS OF A NONFICTION TEXT...

...BUT SUMMARIES CAN ALSO PROVIDE INFORMATION THAT IS NEW, INTERESTING, AND RELEVANT.

REMEMBER #1

SUMMARIZE
to set up CONTEXTS and provide background INFORMATION.

PARAPHRASING
SHOULD GIVE THE READER A MORE COMPLETE SENSE OF THE AUTHOR'S ARGUMENT AND MORE OF THE FLAVOR OF THE ORIGINAL THAN A SUMMARY.

AND EVEN THOUGH A PARAPHRASE IS "IN YOUR OWN WORDS," THE IDEAS CAME FROM SOMEWHERE ELSE -- SO YOU'LL HAVE TO CITE YOUR SOURCE.

HERE'S A PARAPHRASE OF PART OF A CHAPTER IN THE BOOK *CITY OF QUARTZ*, A HISTORY OF LOS ANGELES.

AUTHOR MIKE DAVIS CLAIMS THAT NOIR STORIES ABOUT CRIME AND THE ILL EFFECTS OF CAPITALISM REFLECT MANY DIFFERENT INFLUENCES FROM THE TIME OF THE GREAT DEPRESSION, WORLD WAR II, AND THE PERIOD THAT FOLLOWED.

DAVIS ARGUES THAT IMMIGRANT WRITERS, COMPOSERS, FILMMAKERS, AND ARTISTS FLEEING HITLER'S GERMANY PLAYED A ROLE IN DEVELOPING CERTAIN ASPECTS OF THE NOIR DETECTIVE GENRE, BUT HE INSISTS THAT FEW OF THEM ACTUALLY PARTICIPATED IN THE GRITTY URBAN LIFESTYLES OF LOS ANGELES IN THE 1940s.

UNLIKE MANY CRITICS, DAVIS ASSERTS THAT LOCAL LOS ANGELES AUTHORS PLAYED A MAJOR ROLE IN DEVELOPING WHAT CAME TO BE KNOWN AS "L.A. NOIR."

HE SAYS THAT THESE LOCAL WRITERS KNEW MUCH MORE ABOUT THE SCANDALS OF THE CITY -- POLICE CORRUPTION, REAL ESTATE AND OIL SPECULATION, AND ANTI-LABOR AND ANTI-IMMIGRANT POLITICS -- THAN OUTSIDERS COMING FROM EUROPE DID.

WOW!

THAT PARAPHRASE REALLY GAVE ME A SENSE OF DAVIS'S ARGUMENT AND OF WHY HIS SCHOLARSHIP IS DISTINCTIVE.

SO, WHEN YOU FIND A SOURCE THAT IS REALLY SIGNIFICANT FOR YOUR RESEARCH, EVEN IF YOU DISAGREE WITH IT, YOU MIGHT WANT TO SPEND SOME TIME CAREFULLY PARAPHRASING IT IN YOUR OWN WORDS.

PARAPHRASE

SUMMARY

REMEMBER #2

PARAPHRASE
to give a sense of the author's ARGUMENT.

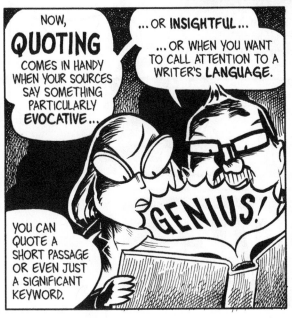

NOW, **QUOTING** COMES IN HANDY WHEN YOUR SOURCES SAY SOMETHING PARTICULARLY **EVOCATIVE**...

...OR **INSIGHTFUL**...

...OR WHEN YOU WANT TO CALL ATTENTION TO A WRITER'S **LANGUAGE**.

GENIUS!

YOU CAN QUOTE A SHORT PASSAGE OR EVEN JUST A SIGNIFICANT KEYWORD.

IF YOU CHOOSE TO PRESENT A LONG QUOTATION, MAKE SURE THAT YOU HAVE ENOUGH TO SAY ABOUT THE PASSAGE TO SHOW WHY IT'S WORTH REPRODUCING IN ITS ENTIRETY.

FOR INSTANCE...

LAUGHING in the JUNGLE
LOUIS ADAMIC

LAUGHING IN THE JUNGLE, A BOOK ABOUT LOS ANGELES BY IMMIGRANT WRITER LOUIS ADAMIC, HAS A DISTINCTIVE WRITING STYLE AND MANY JUICY PASSAGES TO CHOOSE FROM.

HERE ARE ADAMIC'S PROVOCATIVE INSIGHTS ON THE CITY:

"FROM MOUNT HOLLYWOOD, LOS ANGELES LOOKS RATHER NICE....

"ACTUALLY, AND IN SPITE OF ALL THE HEALTHFUL SUNSHINE AND OCEAN BREEZES, IT IS A **BAD** PLACE, FULL OF OLD, DYING PEOPLE, AND YOUNG PEOPLE WHO WERE BORN OLD OF TIRED PIONEER PARENTS, VICTIMS OF AMERICA --

"-- FULL OF CURIOUS WILD AND POISONOUS GROWTHS, DECADENT RELIGIONS AND CULTS AND FAKE SCIENCE, AND WILDCAT BUSINESS ENTERPRISES, WHICH, WITH THEIR AIM FOR QUICK PROFITS, ARE DOOMED TO COLLAPSE AND DRAG DOWN MULTITUDES OF PEOPLE...

"...A JUNGLE."

IF YOU DON'T NEED THE WHOLE QUOTATION, YOU CAN WEAVE SHORT QUOTED DESCRIPTIONS INTO YOUR OWN PROSE.

NOTICE THAT, IN EACH CASE, WE USE QUOTATION MARKS, PROVIDE AN IN-TEXT CITATION (THIS ONE FOLLOWS MLA STYLE), AND EMPHASIZE OUR OWN COMMENTARY.

tap tap

"Adamic gives us verbal images that contradict a popular picture of health. Terms such as 'poisonous,' 'dying,' and 'decadent' (220) provide a stark contrast with the 'sunshine and ocean breezes' typically associated with L.A."

REMEMBER #3

QUOTE
to draw attention to the author's own WORDS and PHRASING.

*In this case, Tom Gammill, creator of The Doozies.

YOU SHOULD **TALK** TO US IF YOU'RE HAVING TROUBLE HANDLING A PROJECT.

PRESENTING OTHERS' WORK AS YOUR OWN IS A TERRIBLE IDEA FOR A LOT OF REASONS.

FOR ONE THING, IT'S **PLAGIARISM**.

BUT JUST A COUPLE OF PAGES BACK YOU GUYS WERE TALKING ABOUT QUOTING FROM SOURCES.

BUT YOU NEED TO TELL READERS WHERE YOU FOUND YOUR SOURCES, NOT PRETEND YOU CREATED THE WORK YOURSELF.

AND YOU ALSO NEED TO EVALUATE AND INTERPRET MATERIAL THAT YOU FIND AND INTEGRATE IT INTO YOUR OWN TEXT.

YOU DON'T JUST INSERT SOURCES WITHOUT ANY ANALYSIS OR REFLECTION!

IF YOU ARE GOING TO QUOTE SOMEONE ELSE'S WORK, HAVE A GOOD REASON FOR REPRODUCING IT EXACTLY.

=SIGH=

THAT MAKES SENSE.

I GUESS WE KNEW ALL THAT, BUT DESPERATION MAKES PEOPLE DO CRAZY THINGS SOMETIMES.

IT'S NOT ALWAYS EASY TO CITE YOUR SOURCES.

OUR STUDENTS HAVE TROUBLE WITH IT ALL THE TIME.

HOW DO I CITE A VIDEO I WATCHED **ONLINE**?

WHAT ABOUT A **COMIC**?

Issue 6 • Research: More Than Detective Work

REFRAME
with
Luis & Cindy

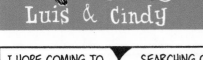

Wrong turns or shortcuts?

I HOPE COMING TO THE LIBRARY WASN'T A WASTE OF TIME.

SEARCHING ON GOOGLE MIGHT WORK JUST AS WELL.

DEPENDS ON THE SUBJECT, I GUESS.

WHAT ARE YOU WORKING ON?

A PROJECT ON FRACKING.

IT'S A TECHNIQUE FOR EXTRACTING NATURAL GAS FROM ROCK.

STOP!

NO FRACK

NO

FRACK

BOO!

I KNOW. THEY USE HIGH-PRESSURE FLUIDS.

IT'S CONTROVERSIAL BECAUSE SOME PEOPLE ARE CONCERNED ABOUT ENVIRONMENTAL CONSEQUENCES.

MEANWHILE...

bloop bloop bloop

COME ON...

bloop... bloop... BANG!

1-up!

YES!

WITH YOUR FIRST SEARCH, YOU FOUND A HUGE RANGE OF TOPICS FOR DIFFERENT AUDIENCES.

YOU SHOULD GIVE THE "ADVANCED SEARCH" OPTIONS A SHOT TO FOCUS YOUR SEARCH.

TRY **FRACKING** AS AN ITEM TITLE SO THAT THE WORD HAS TO BE PART OF THE TITLE.

ADVANCED SEARCH CAN ALSO LIMIT THE RESULTS TO ARTICLES.

JSTOR

ADVANCED SEARCH

JSTOR HOME SEARCH ▾ BROWSE ▾ MyJSTOR ▾

26 Search Results

ti:fracking OR tb:fracking   Search   Modify Search   Search Help

☐ Search within results

Content Type: All Types   Access Options: All Content   Sort By: Relevance   Export Selected Citations

☐ Get Fracking
Thomas K. Grose
ASEE Prism, Vol. 21, No. 1 (SEPTEMBER 2011), pp. 40-43
[Journal]

...about technological advances of gallons of water mixed with sand and chemicals - some toxic - to that make it economical to extract create fissures. **Fracking** is not new; the industry has used it in oil vast amounts of natural gas from shale wells for around 60 years. In the 1980s...

Download PDF
Add To My Lists
Cite This Item

☐ Fracking fury
Janna Palliser
Science Scope, Vol. 35, No. 7, ENVIRONMENTAL CHANGE (MARCH 2012), pp. 20-24
[Journal]

...BaSBBIIsiENCE **Fracking** fury by Janna PalHiser Hydraulic also ing." ing" known seems or "hydrofrack- fracturing, as to "frack- be ev- also known as "frack- ing" or "hydrofrack- ing," seems to be ev- erywhere these days. Reports on major news networks, on Nation- al Public Radio, and online are aplenty. There have...

Download PDF
Add To My Lists
Cite This Item

☐ "Fracking:" A Roundtable
Ronald E. Bishop, David J. Lampe, Brian W. Okey, Tom Wilber, Myron Arnowitt
Journal of Appalachian Studies, Vol. 18, No. 1/2 (Spring/Fall 2012), pp. 31-47
[Journal]

..." to represent the entire range of shale gas development processes (Vandenberg et al 2012), industry proponents generally reject such broad definitions, restricting their use of the terms "hydraulic fracturing" or " **fracking** " to those short segments of time when high pressures are being applied to deep rock formations...

Download PDF
Add To My Lists
Cite This Item

POE TRY

APPALACHIAN STUDIES APPEARS AGAIN, SO TAKE A CLOSER LOOK. IT **IS** A PEER-REVIEWED JOURNAL.

BUT IT PUBLISHES **LITERARY CRITICISM** AS WELL AS EMPIRICAL RESEARCH, SO IT MIGHT NOT BE THE BEST PLACE FOR FINDING SCIENTIFIC DATA OR MATERIAL ABOUT THE LEGAL ISSUES SURROUNDING FRACKING.

LET'S TRY A SEARCH USING PRECISE TECHNICAL TERMS.

WHAT SHOULD I ENTER?

HMM...

CINDY, WHAT DO YOU THINK WOULD BE A GOOD--

CINDY?

click click

COME ON...

WOOT!

I TOOK OUT THE HYDRAULIC FRACKER!

BING! BING!

UH, HOW ABOUT "HYDRAULIC FRACTURING" RATHER THAN "FRACKING"?

GOOD IDEA.

SOMETIMES QUOTATION MARKS IMPROVE RESULTS.

THEY LIMIT RESULTS TO THE SPECIFIC PHRASE CONTAINED WITHIN THE QUOTES.

"hydraulic

HMM. THAT'S STILL A LOT.

WHEN YOU GET SEVERAL SEARCH RESULTS, YOU SHOULD LOOK BEYOND JUST THE FIRST FEW. MAKE SURE TO SCROLL DOWN.

RESULTS

Hydraulic Fracturing: Risks and Risk Management

Thomas Swartz

Natural Resources & Environment, Vol. 26, No. 2, oil & gas:
POST-DEEPWATER HORIZON (Fall 2011), pp. 30-32, 59

[Journal]

The facts behind the FRACK: Scientists weigh in on the hydraulic fracturing debate

Rachel Ehrenberg

Science News, Vol. 182, No. 5 (SEPTEMBER 8, 2012), pp. 20-25

[Journal]

Tracking Fracking Case Law: Hydraulic Fracturing Litigation

Barclay Nicholson, Kadian Blanson

Natural Resources & Environment, Vol. 26, No. 2, oil & gas:
POST-DEEPWATER HORIZON (Fall 2011), pp. 25-29

[Journal]

legislation/regulation: Hydraulic Fracturing: Is Regulation Needed?

Frederick W. Pontius

Journal (American Water Works Association), Vol. 101, No. 9 (September 2009). p. 24, 26, 28, 30, 32

[Journal]

Stress Determination by Hydraulic Fracturing in Subsurface Waste Injection

R. G. Wolff, J. D. Bredehoeft, W. S. Keys, Eugene Shuter

Journal (American Water Works Association), Vol. 67, No. 9, Ground-Water
Recharge (September 1975), pp. 519-523

[Journal]

The Crack Tip Region in Hydraulic Fracturing

J. Desroches, E. Detournay, B. Lenoach, P. Papanastasiou, J. R. A. Pearson, M. Thiercelin,
A. Cheng

Proceedings: Mathematical and Physical Sciences, Vol. 447, No. 1929 (Oct. 8, 1994), pp. 39-48

[Journal]

A Community Divided: Hydraulic Fracturing in Rural Appalachia

Michele Morrone, Amy E. Chadwick, Natalie Kruse

Journal of Appalachian Studies, Vol. 21, No. 2 (Fall 2015). pp. 207-228

[Journal]

Stress Determination by Hydraulic Fracturing in Subsurface Waste Injection

R. G. Wolff, J. D. Bredehoeft, W. S. Keys, Eugene Shuter

Journal (American Water Works Association), Vol. 67, No. 9, Ground-Water Recharge (September 1975), pp. 519-523

legislation/regulation: Hydraulic Fracturing: Is Regulation Needed?

Frederick W. Pontius

Journal (American Water Works Association), Vol. 101, No. 9 (September 2009), p. 24, 26, 28, 30, 32

TWO OF THESE ARTICLES ARE FROM A JOURNAL FROM THE AMERICAN WATER WORKS ASSOCIATION.

IT MIGHT TAKE SOME INVESTIGATING TO LEARN HOW OBJECTIVE THOSE ARTICLES ARE.

YEAH, IT'S TIME TO DIG DEEPER!

click! click! ding!

ha ha

I'M ALMOST AT THE DEPOSIT!

+500

ANYWAY... ...YOU CAN SEARCH JUST FOR THE PEER-REVIEWED ARTICLES FROM THAT JOURNAL, WHICH CAN BE SEPARATED FROM FEATURE ARTICLES ON WATER MANAGEMENT OR INDUSTRY NEWS.

YOU CAN ALSO DO SOME RESEARCH ON THE ORGANIZATION. HERE'S WHAT THEIR WEB SITE SAYS:

Established in 1881, the American Water Works Association is the largest nonprofit, scientific and educational association dedicated to managing and treating water, the world's most important resource.

BUT A NONPROFIT ORGANIZATION ISN'T NECESSARILY OBJECTIVE.

HOW ABOUT THIS...

SEARCHING ABSTRACTS MAY GENERATE FEWER RESULTS, BUT THEY MAY BE MORE ON TARGET. TRY SEARCHING FOR "HYDRAULIC FRACTURING" IN THE ABSTRACT RATHER THAN FULL TEXT.

PNAS

Methane contamination of drinking water accompanying gas-well drilling and hydraulic fracturing

Author(s): Stephen G. Osborn, Avner Vengosh, Nathaniel R. Warner and Robert B. Jackson

Source: *Proceedings of the National Academy of Sciences of the United States of America*, Vol. 108, No. 20 (May 17, 2011), pp. 8172-8176

Published by: National Academy of Sciences

Stable URL: http://www.jstor.org/stable/25830023

Accessed: 20-10-2016 20:41 UTC

Methane contamination of drinking water accompanying gas-well drilling and hydraulic fracturing

Stephen G. Osborn[a], Avner Vengosh[b], Nathaniel R. Warner[b], and Robert B. Jackson[a,b,c,1]

[a]Center on Global Change, Nicholas School of the Environment, [b]Division of Earth and Ocean Sciences, Nicholas School of [c]Biology Department, Duke University, Durham, NC 27708

Edited[*] by William H. Schlesinger, Cary Institute of Ecosystem Studies, Millbrook, NY, and approved April 14, 2011 (receiv

Directional drilling and hydraulic-fracturing technologies are dramatically increasing natural-gas extraction. In aquifers overlying the Marcellus and Utica shale formations of northeastern Pennsylvania and upstate New York, we document systematic evidence for methane contamination of drinking water associated with shale-gas extraction. In active gas-extraction areas (one or more gas wells within 1 km), average and maximum methane concentrations

THE NATIONAL ACADEMY OF SCIENCES IS A LEADING ORGANIZATION OF SCIENTISTS KNOWN FOR THEIR PEER-REVIEWED RESEARCH THAT MEETS RIGOROUS STANDARDS. PROCEEDINGS COLLECT MAJOR PRESENTATIONS FROM SCHOLARLY CONFERENCES.

ALMOST... THERE...

AAAGHHHH!!

next 50 years with current technologies. *Science* 305:968–972.
2. Tour JM, Kittrell C, Colvin VL (2010) Green carbon as a bridge to renewable energy. *Nature Mater* 9:871–874.
3. Kerr RA (2010) Natural gas from shale bursts onto the scene. *Science* 328:1624–1626.
4. Raupach MR, et al. (2007) Global and regional drivers of accelerating CO₂ emissions. *Proc Natl Acad Sci USA* 104:10288–10293.
5. US Energy Information Administration (2010) *Annual Energy Outlook 2010 with Projections to 2035* (US Energy Information Administration, Washington, DC), DOE/EIA-0383; http://www.eia.doe.gov/oiaf/aeo/pdf/0383(2010).pdf.
6. US Environmental Protection Agency (2011) Hydraulic Fracturing. (US Environmental Protection Agency, Washington, DC), http://water.epa.gov/type/groundwater/uic/class2/hydraulicfracturing/.
7. Kargbo DM, Wilhelm RG, Campbell DJ (2010) Natural gas plays in the Marcellus shale: Challenges and potential opportunities. *Environ Sci Technol* 44:5679–5684.
8. Revesz KM, Breen KJ, Baldassare AJ, Burruss RC (2010) Carbon and hydrogen isotopic evidence for the origin of combustible gases in water-supply wells in north-central Pennsylvania. *Appl Geochem* 25:1845–1859.
9. Zoback M, Kitasei S, Copithorne B Addressing the environmental risks from shale gas development. *Worldwatch Institute Briefing Paper 1* (Worldwatch Inst, Washington, DC), http://blogs.worldwatch.org/revolt/wp-content/uploads/2010/07/Environmental-Risks-Paper-July-2010-FOR-PRINT.pdf.
10. Pennsylvania Department of Environmental Protection, Bureau of Oil and Gas Management (2010) *2009 Year End Workload Report*. (Pennsylvania Dept of Environmental Protection, Bureau of Oil and Gas Management, Harrisburg, PA), http://www.dep.state.pa.us/dep/deputate/minres/oilgas/2009%20Year%20End%20Report-WEBSITE.pdf.
11. Colborn T, Kwiatkowski C, Schultz K, Bachran M (2010) Natural gas operations from a public health perspective. *Hum Ecol Risk Assess*, in press.
12. Pennsylvania Department of Environmental Protection (2011) Private Water Wells in Pennsylvania. (Pennsylvania Dept of Environmental Protection, Harrisburg, PA), http://www.dep.state.pa.us/dep/deputate/watermg/wc/Subjects/Srce/Prot/well/.
13. Eltschlager KK, Hawkins JW, Ehler WC, Baldassare F (2001) *Technical Measures for the Investigation and Mitigation of Fugitive Methane Hazards in Areas of Coal Mining* (US Dept of the Interior, Office of Surface Mining Reclamation and Enforcement, Pittsburgh).
14. Schoell M (1980) The hydrogen and carbon isotopic composition of methane from natural gases of various origins. *Geochim Cosmochim Acta* 44:649–661.
15. Bernard BB (1978) Light hydrocarbons in marine sediments. PhD Dissertation (Texas A&M Univ, College Station, TX).
16. Jenden PD, Drazan DJ, Kaplan IR (1993) Mixing of thermogenic natural gases in northern Appalachian Basin. *Am Assoc Pet Geol Bull* 77:980–998.
17. Laughrey CD, Baldassare FJ (1998) Geochemistry and origin of some natural gases in the Plateau Province Central Appalachian Basin, Pennsylvania and Ohio. *Am Assoc Pet Geol Bull* 82:317–335.
18. Osborn SG, McIntosh JC (2010) Chemical and isotopic tracers of the contribution of microbial gas in Devonian organic-rich shales and reservoir sandstones, northern Appalachian Basin. *Appl Geochem* 25:456–471.
19. Repetski JE, Ryder RT, Harper JA, Trippi MH (2006) Thermal maturity patterns in the Ordovician and Devonian of Pennsylvania using conodont color alteration index (CAI) and vitrinite reflectance (%Ro). *Northeastern Geology Environmental Sciences*

and biogenic methane: Upper Devonia *Cosmochim Acta* 62:1699–1720.
21. Engelder T, Lash GG, Uzcategui RS (2 Middle and Upper Devonian gas shale *Bull* 93:857–889.
22. Pennsylvania Department of Environr Environmental Protection, Harrisburg pa.us/dep/deputate/minres/oilgas/new
23. New York State Department of Health (2009) (New York State Dept of Health mental Generic Environmental Stater Well Permit Issuance for Horizontal the Marcellus Shale and other Lc riverkeeper.org/wp-content/uploads/20 3-NYSDOH-Environmental-Radiation-M
24. Taylor LE (1984) Groundwater Resourc sylvania: Water Resources Report 58. (Office of Parks and Forestry—Bureau o PA) 139.
25. Williams JH, Taylor L, Low D (1998) H Glaciated Valleys of Bradford, Tioga, sources Report 68. (Commonwealth of Resources, Harrisburg, PA) p 89.
26. Kendall C, Coplan TB (2001) Distributi across the United States. *Hydrol Proc*
27. Van Stempvoort D, Maathuis H, Jaw fugitive methane in groundwater link 43:187–199.
28. Taylor SW, Sherwood Lollar B, Wass surface aquifers: Implications for leak 34:4727–4732.
29. Cramer B, Schlomer S, Poelchau HS (2 the release of natural gas from groun tions, London), 447–455.
30. Geyer AR, Wilshusen JP (1982) Engine environmental geology supplement Geological Survey. (Dept of Environm ment, Harrisburg, PA).

31. le G, Martinelli G (2002) Migration of carrier a overview. *Phys Earth Planet Inter* 129:185–204.
32. Aravena R, Wassenaar LI (1993) Dissolved organic ca confined aquifer, southern Ontario, Canada: Carbor subsurfa rces. *Appl Geochem* 8:483–493.
33. Colem D, Liu C, Riley KM (1988) Microbial me sed lacial deposits of the Illinois, USA.
34. A R, Doden AG, Gold DP, Root SI/2

COMING UP IN THE NEXT EXCITING EPISODE OF **REFRAME**

"Am I MISSING something?" [pg 279]

WALK the TALK

"RESEARCH"

1 CONNECTIONS

TO GET STARTED AS A RESEARCHER, LOOK FOR AN ENTRY POINT THAT APPEALS TO YOU. YOU CAN LOOK AT A VARIETY OF BACKGROUND SOURCES OR BEGIN WITH A PERSONAL CONNECTION THAT DRAWS YOU TO YOUR TOPIC.

MARISSA OSATO WANTED TO RESEARCH JAPANESE INTERNMENT CAMPS DURING WORLD WAR II BECAUSE OF A PERSONAL CONNECTION: HER GRANDMOTHER HAD LIVED IN ONE OF THE CAMPS.

IDEAS AND SOURCES CAN LEAD TO UNEXPECTED PLACES. YOUR RESEARCH MIGHT EVEN END UP HELPING OTHER RESEARCHERS SOMEDAY!

SEE WHERE **YOUR** RESEARCH TAKES YOU.

Gesensway, Deborah, and Mindy Roseman. *Beyond Words: Images from America's Concentration Camps.* Cornell UP, 1987.

Kuramitsu, Kristine C. "Internment and Identity in Japanese American Art." *American Quarterly*, vol. 47, no. 4, Dec. 1995, pp. 619-58. JSTOR, doi:10.2307/2713369.

Matsuda, Ted. "Contemporary Accounts and Documents (Photocopies), 1942-1976 and Undated." Mitsuye Yamada Papers, MS-R71, Box 1, Folder 6, Special Collections and Archives, The U California Irvine Libraries, Irvine.

Osato, Mollie. Bird pins. Circa 1943-45. Photograph by Marissa Osato.

Osato, Mollie. Personal interview. 14 May 2006.

Something Strong Within. Directed by Robert A. Nakamura, Japanese American National Museum, 1994.

DRAWING CONCLUSIONS

The following assignments ask you to practice finding, evaluating, and responding to research sources.

1 Look at Liz's detective map on p. 221. Try to follow the arrows and construct a version of her investigation, writing out a step-by-step narrative that describes the process.

Think about the organization of your details, and craft a story that makes some kind of sense even when the illustrations are outlandish.

2 Choose a current event that you already know a little bit about, and spend some time gathering what you believe are unreliable resources on that topic -- perhaps a biased news site or a personal blog.

Once you've gathered some examples, try to think of instances in which these resources might be useful, depending on what aspect of the event is being discussed.

On the other end of the spectrum, are there ever instances when "reputable" sources of information might **NOT** be suitable for a particular piece of writing?

3

Choose a historical event and search for as many different kinds of sources on the topic as you can -- primary and secondary, fiction and nonfiction, multimedia, digital, etc.

As you gather your list, brainstorm ways you can evaluate the usefulness or relevance of each source. What are your methods for finding different sources? What kinds of sources are easier or more difficult to find?

4

A good way to begin creating a research-based argument is to find a position that you will refute or critique. Think about your position on some significant aspect of the event you began researching in question 3.

Find a source that takes a thoughtful position that differs from your own. Summarize that source's argument fairly, and then sketch out a chart or an outline of your response.

ISSUE 7
RETHINKING REVISION
In this issue...
LOOKING BEYOND THE RED INK
Page 260
REVIEWING RHETORICALLY
Page 265
SEEING THROUGH OTHERS' EYES
Page 268
REVISING RADICALLY
Page 272
ital
SP
stet
bf
fr
-30-

THAT'S NOT WHAT WE WANT TO SHOW PEOPLE ABOUT **REVISION.**

YEAH, REVISION ISN'T JUST ABOUT CORRECTING **MISTAKES.**

IT MEANS EXACTLY WHAT IT SAYS:

"RE-VISION."

IT'S ABOUT SEEING A COMPOSITION ANEW, WITH FRESH EYES --

-- SEEING YOUR OWN WORK AS IF YOU WERE ANOTHER READER.

IT'S ABOUT CONSIDERING POSSIBILITIES...

...AS WELL AS PROBLEMS.

LOOKING FOR ERRORS THAT ARE DISTRACTING, EVEN IF THEY DON'T SERIOUSLY INTERFERE WITH READERS' UNDERSTANDING, IS ONLY THE MOST BASIC FORM OF REVISION.

COME BACK SOON!

FASHION!

BUT EVEN IF FLAWS AREN'T SERIOUS, THEY CAN MAKE YOU LOOK **TERRIBLE.**

YOU CAN'T JUST IGNORE WHAT EVERYONE CAN SEE PLAINLY.

PEOPLE MIGHT NOT SAY ANY-THING TO YOUR FACE, BUT THEY WILL CERTAINLY JUDGE YOU IF YOU LOOK BAD.

SO-CALLED "SURFACE ERRORS" CAN BE A TURN-OFF TO AUDIENCES.

LIKE *ITS* AND *IT'S.* WHY CAN'T PEOPLE GET THAT RIGHT?

OR *THEIR, THEY'RE,* AND *THERE.*

Delete

I HATE THAT MISTAKE.

LOOK, WE UNDERSTAND.

WE'RE WRITING TEACHERS. WE SEE MISTAKES ALL DAY LONG.

POP! POP!

PLEASE COME AGAIN

FASHION!

SOME COMMON ERRORS ARE ALSO VERY DISTRACTING.

OUR FRIEND ELLEN STRENSKI CALLS THESE "NOSE-PICKING ERRORS."

SUCH ERRORS SEEM TO INDICATE A LACK OF SELF-AWARENESS.

AND THEY SIGNAL THAT THE PEOPLE WHO MAKE THEM EITHER DON'T KNOW CONVENTIONS OF ACADEMIC WRITING OR WON'T SHOW THEIR AUDIENCES ENOUGH RESPECT TO EDIT THE WORK CAREFULLY.

SOME PEOPLE FIND THESE ERRORS SO REPULSIVE THAT THEY CAN'T PAY ATTENTION TO THE MESSAGE BEING DELIVERED.

THESE PEOPLE MAY BE OVERLY SENSITIVE ABOUT IMPERFECTION...

CENSORED

...BUT YOU WANT TO AVOID UNINTENTIONALLY CREATING STRONG NEGATIVE REACTIONS TO YOUR WRITING.

263

PRETTY MUCH ALL OF THE BOOKS IN THIS LIBRARY WERE REVISED DURING THE DRAFTING PROCESS IN WAYS THAT WENT FAR BEYOND SIMPLY FIXING SPELLING AND GRAMMATICAL MISTAKES.

SEE THIS BOOK?

IT'S PERSUASION, JANE AUSTEN'S LAST NOVEL. THE INITIAL DRAFT OF THIS BOOK HAD A COMPLETELY DIFFERENT ENDING.

Persuasion
JANE AUSTEN
1775-1817

THE ORIGINAL ENDING DIDN'T HAVE THE WITTY DIALOGUE OR THE OBSERVATIONS ABOUT HUMAN CHARACTER THAT AUSTEN WAS KNOWN FOR.

Sense and Sensibility
Emma
Pride and Prejudice

265

THE FIRST VERSION OF AUSTEN'S HAPPY ENDING COMES ABOUT BECAUSE THE HEROINE IS TRICKED INTO BEING ALONE WITH THE HERO. WHEN HE DECLARES HIS LOVE FOR HER IN VERY CONVENTIONAL LANGUAGE, SHE DOESN'T HAVE MUCH TO SAY IN RESPONSE.

BECAUSE AUSTEN WASN'T HAPPY WITH THE ENDING OF HER NOVEL, SHE REVISED RADICALLY.

SHE CREATED A BRAND-NEW SCENE IN WHICH A LOT WAS GOING ON BECAUSE THE CHARACTERS IN THE STORY WERE PREPARING FOR A WEDDING.

Mary and Henrietta heading out the front door for a walk.

Mrs. Musgrove giving Mrs. Croft the history of her eldest daughter's engagement.

Captain Wentworth secretly writing a love letter to Anne.

Captain Harville and Anne arguing about whether men or women are more faithful.

Persuasion

IN THE REVISED ENDING, AUSTEN'S HEROINE SHOWS HERSELF TO BE A SOPHISTICATED CONVERSATIONALIST IN A DEBATE ABOUT WHETHER MEN OR WOMEN ARE MORE FAITHFUL IN LOVE.

ALTHOUGH HE DOESN'T SEEM TO BE PAYING ATTENTION, THE DASHING HERO IS ACTUALLY LISTENING TO HER ARGUMENT ATTENTIVELY.

WHILE ALL THE ACTION IS GOING ON AROUND HIM, HE WRITES HER A LETTER TO TELL HER HOW HE REALLY FEELS.

I DEFINITELY LIKE THAT ENDING BETTER.

IT IS A LOT MORE RHETORICALLY INTERESTING.

OF COURSE, A MORE ELABORATE SOLUTION TO A PROBLEM IN A PIECE OF WRITING ISN'T ALWAYS THE RIGHT APPROACH.

SOMETIMES A SIMPLER SOLUTION IS BETTER.

TEMPUS FUGIT

BUT WHETHER YOU'RE REVISING A NOVEL OR A PIECE OF ACADEMIC WRITING...

...IT'S IMPORTANT TO GIVE YOURSELF ENOUGH TIME TO MAKE MAJOR REVISIONS, AS AUSTEN DID.

SEEING THROUGH OTHERS' EYES

OFTEN WRITERS CONSULT OTHER WRITERS FOR HELP WHEN MAKING A MAJOR REVISION.

IN A WRITING CLASS, THIS PROCESS MIGHT BE CALLED "PEER EDITING" OR "PEER REVISION."

U.S. PRESIDENT ABRAHAM LINCOLN'S SECRETARY OF STATE, WILLIAM SEWARD, WAS VERY IMPORTANT IN THE REVISION OF LINCOLN'S MAJOR SPEECHES.

SEWARD THOUGHT THAT IT WAS IMPORTANT FOR LINCOLN'S FIRST INAUGURAL SPEECH TO AVOID A CONFRONTATIONAL TONE THAT WOULD ANGER THE LOSING CANDIDATE'S SUPPORTERS.

SPEECHES of ABRAHAM LINCOLN

HE WORRIED THAT LINCOLN MIGHT SAY SOMETHING THAT COULD BE INTERPRETED AS AN EXCUSE FOR THE SOUTH TO SECEDE FROM THE UNION.

ABRAHAM LINCOLN (1809–1865)
16th PRESIDENT OF THE UNITED STATES

WILLIAM HENRY SEWARD (1801–1872)
SECRETARY OF STATE

SEWARD WAS RIGHT TO BE WORRIED. LINCOLN'S EARLY DRAFTS FOR THE INAUGURAL ADDRESS WERE EXTREMELY CONFRONTATIONAL.

In your hands, my dissatisfied fellow countrymen, and not in mine, is the momentous issue of civil war. The government will not assail you, unless you first assail it. You can have no conflict, without being yourselves the aggressors. You have no oath registered in Heaven to destroy the government, while I shall have the most solemn one to "preserve, protect, and defend" it. You can forbear the assault upon it; I can not shrink from the defense of it. With you, and not with me, is the solemn question of "Shall it be peace, or a sword?"

HE'S PRACTICALLY DARING SLAVEHOLDING STATES TO REVOLT.

"SHALL IT BE PEACE, OR A SWORD?" WHAT A TERRIBLE ENDING!

WHAT IS HE **THINKING**?

SEWARD LATER EXPLAINED WHAT HE SAW AS THE FLAW IN LINCOLN'S ORIGINAL APPROACH:

...we must CHANGE THE QUESTION BEFORE THE PUBLIC FROM ONE UPON SLAVERY, OR ABOUT SLAVERY, for a question upon UNION OR DISUNION.

SEWARD KNEW THAT THE FINAL WORDS OF THE SPEECH WERE GOING TO HAVE THE MOST RHETORICAL IMPACT. SO HE OFFERED THE PRESIDENT SOME DIFFERENT OPTIONS FOR WORDING AND SUGGESTED TWO DIFFERENT ENDINGS.

LIKE ANY GOOD PEER REVIEWER, SEWARD GAVE HIS PARTNER SOME CHOICES.

LINCOLN LIKED THE SECOND OF SEWARD'S SUGGESTED CLOSING PARAGRAPHS BETTER.

The mystic chords which proceeding from so many battle fields and so many patriot graves pass through all the hearts and all the hearths in this broad continent of ours will yet again harmonize in their ancient music when breathed upon by the guardian angel of the nation.

LINCOLN APPROVED OF SEWARD'S COMPLEX METAPHOR OF A MUSICAL STRING CONNECTING TWO POINTS.

THIS RHETORICAL FIGURE REPRESENTED THE EMOTIONAL BOND CONNECTING THE GRAVES OF REVOLUTIONARY SOLDIERS TO THE PEOPLE OF LINCOLN'S OWN DAY.

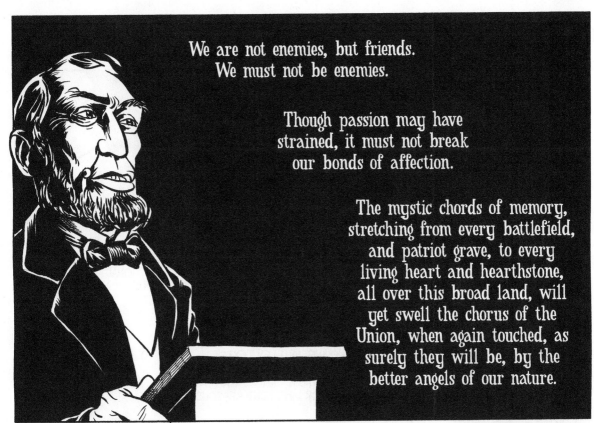

We are not enemies, but friends.
We must not be enemies.

Though passion may have
strained, it must not break
our bonds of affection.

The mystic chords of memory,
stretching from every battlefield,
and patriot grave, to every
living heart and hearthstone,
all over this broad land, will
yet swell the chorus of the
Union, when again touched, as
surely they will be, by the
better angels of our nature.

WHEN YOUR OWN WORK IS REVIEWED BY OTHER PEOPLE, IT CAN BE IMPORTANT TO EVALUATE THEIR SUGGESTIONS.

ACCEPTING ALL ADVICE FROM OTHERS UNCRITICALLY CAN BE ALMOST AS BAD AS REFUSING TO LISTEN TO FEEDBACK IN THE FIRST PLACE.

BE AN ACTIVE PARTICIPANT IN YOUR REVISION PROCESS AT EVERY STAGE OF DRAFTING.

REVISING RADICALLY

LINCOLN WAS A FAMOUSLY CREATIVE **REVISER**.

LINCOLN'S DRAFTS

HE OFTEN HAD DRAFTS OF HIS SPEECHES PRINTED, SO HE COULD SEE THE LANGUAGE NOT IN HIS OWN HANDWRITING.

THEN HE WOULD CUT UP THESE PRINTED DRAFTS AND REARRANGE THEM.

HE WOULD ALSO SPLICE IN ADDITIONAL HANDWRITTEN REVISIONS.

A LOT HAS CHANGED SINCE THESE REVISERS DEVELOPED THEIR OWN PERSONAL STRATEGIES FOR IMPROVING WRITTEN TEXTS.

REMEMBER THAT THESE FAMOUS WRITERS WERE REVISING FOR DIFFERENT REASONS.

JANE AUSTEN (1775–1817)

ABRAHAM LINCOLN (1809–1865)

AUSTEN WANTED TO IMPROVE HER NARRATIVE AND SOLVE A STRUCTURAL PROBLEM.

LINCOLN WAS FOCUSING ON PERSUADING A SKEPTICAL AUDIENCE.

REVISE REVISE

WE ENCOURAGE YOU TO THINK ABOUT REVISION RADICALLY.

SOMETIMES WRITERS HAVE TO MAKE RADICAL REVISIONS FOR REASONS NOT OF THEIR OWN CHOOSING.

TONIGHT: 7pm Maxine Hong Kingston

WHEN THE MANUSCRIPT OF WRITER MAXINE HONG KINGSTON'S NOVEL-IN-PROGRESS BURNED IN 1991, ALONG WITH HER HOUSE AND ALL HER POSSESSIONS, SHE HAD TO RECONSTITUTE MATERIAL FROM MEMORY. SHE CHOSE TO INCORPORATE THE STORY OF THE FIRE INTO THE FINAL VERSION OF HER NOVEL, CALLED *THE FIFTH BOOK OF PEACE*.

OF COURSE, THIS EXPERIENCE WAS TRAUMATIC FOR KINGSTON.

BUT IT ALSO SHOWS HOW DESTRUCTION MAY SOMETIMES BE A PART OF THE CREATIVE PROCESS.

YOU MIGHT ASK YOURSELF:

IF I COULD ONLY SAVE ONE PARAGRAPH OF THE WORK I'M WRITING, WHICH ONE WOULD I SAVE?

WHICH ONE WOULD I LET GO FIRST?

Cutting and pasting text on a computer screen may seem monotonous, so you might try printing out your work and physically moving the pieces...

AS YOU REVISE, THINK ABOUT WHETHER THE CHOICES YOU'RE MAKING IN THIS WRITING PROJECT FOLLOW THE RHETORICAL ADVICE IN OTHER CHAPTERS OF THIS BOOK.

PAY ATTENTION TO THE APPEALS TO ETHOS, LOGOS, AND PATHOS* IN THE WORK THAT YOU COMPOSE.

*For more on these appeals, see CHAPTER 1.

DO YOUR RHETORICAL CHOICES PRESENT YOU AS A TRUSTWORTHY WRITER?

IS YOUR REASONING PRESENTED LOGICALLY?

ARE YOU ATTENTIVE TO HOW YOU MOVE THE EMOTIONS OF YOUR AUDIENCE?

HOW WILL YOUR WORK BE READ BY A READER VERY DIFFERENT FROM YOURSELF*?

THINK ABOUT THAT PERSON'S EXPECTATIONS CAREFULLY.

*For more on ideal readers, see CHAPTER 2.

DOES YOUR OWN READING OF THE SOURCES THAT YOU INCORPORATE REPRESENT YOUR BEST ANALYTICAL WORK?

REMEMBER, DON'T KEEP YOUR IDENTITY* A SECRET IF YOU WANT TO SAVE THE WORLD WITH YOUR WRITING.

*For more on identity, see CHAPTER 3.

*For more on argument, see CHAPTER 4.

*For more on collaboration, see CHAPTER 5.

YOU MIGHT THINK IT'S TOO LATE TO KEEP INVESTIGATING, BUT RESEARCH* IS AN IMPORTANT PART OF THE REVISION PROCESS.

ARE THERE ANY SOURCES THAT YOU HAVE OVERLOOKED?

ARE THERE ANY SOURCES THAT CAN'T BE TRUSTED?

AND HAVE YOU CREDITED ALL THE DETECTIVE WORK THAT ISN'T YOUR OWN?

*For more on research, see CHAPTER 6.

SOMETIMES IT IS HELPFUL TO FOCUS ON **ADDING**. ARE THERE PARTS OF THE ARGUMENT THAT SEEM UNDERDEVELOPED?

READ YOUR DRAFT AND THINK ABOUT WHAT QUESTIONS YOUR WRITING POSES -- YOU CAN EVEN WRITE THEM IN THE MARGINS.

DO ANY OF THESE QUESTIONS NEED TO BE ANSWERED?

IF SO, YOU MAY NEED TO DO FURTHER THINKING OR RESEARCH.

CHECK YOUR SOURCES CAREFULLY.

HAVE YOU CITED EVERYTHING THAT NEEDS TO BE CITED?

ARE YOUR IN-TEXT AND BIBLIOGRAPHIC CITATIONS IN ORDER?

REMEMBER THAT YOU SHOULD INVEST TIME IN READING YOUR OWN WORK CRITICALLY.

REFRAME with Luis & Cindy

Am I **MISSING** something?

WRITING CENTER

HEY, CINDY, WHAT'S UP?

WELL, I JUST MET WITH THE INSTRUCTOR FOR MY ART HISTORY CLASS, AND NOW I NEED HELP.

SEE, IT'S --

YANK!

WAIT A MINUTE...

...YOU'RE COMING TO THE WRITING CENTER FOR AN **ART HISTORY** PAPER?

YES, OF COURSE!

JONATHAN SAID WE COULD TAKE **ANY** KIND OF WRITING TO THE WRITING CENTER -- NOT JUST ENGLISH PAPERS.

YANK BACK!

SIGH...

AND MY INSTRUCTOR SAYS I HAVE TO REVISE THE **WHOLE** PROJECT.

WRITING CENTER

FINE. HERE.
WRITING CENTER

WHAT'S **WRONG** WITH IT?

THERE'S NOT A **SINGLE GRAMMATICAL ERROR** IN THAT INTRODUCTION.

UHH... MAYBE "SINCE THE DAWN OF TIME" IS A LITTLE TOO **GENERAL**?

WHAT ARE YOU **REALLY** WRITING ABOUT?

FROM THESE FIRST FEW SENTENCES, IT COULD BE PRETTY MUCH **ANYTHING**.

CAVE PAINTINGS. ISN'T IT **OBVIOUS**? IT SAYS RIGHT HERE...

WELL, YOU **DO** MENTION CAVE ART, BUT I CAN'T TELL WHAT YOU WANT TO SAY ABOUT IT. WHAT MAKES IT SPECIAL, OR UNIQUE?

THAT'S PRETTY MUCH WHAT MY INSTRUCTOR SAID.

WRITING CENTER

CINDY?

YOUR TURN!

SO, CINDY, WHAT ARE YOU WORKING ON?

MY PROJECT FOR ART HISTORY. THE INSTRUCTOR SAID IT "LACKED FOCUS."

WELL, LET'S START AT THE BEGINNING. DO YOU HAVE THE PROMPT FOR THE ASSIGNMENT?

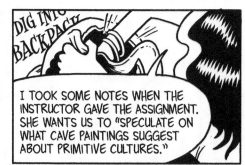

DIG INTO BACKPACK

I TOOK SOME NOTES WHEN THE INSTRUCTOR GAVE THE ASSIGNMENT. SHE WANTS US TO "SPECULATE ON WHAT CAVE PAINTINGS SUGGEST ABOUT PRIMITIVE CULTURES."

HERE WE GO.

LET'S SEE WHAT YOU'VE GOT SO FAR.

HMM...

YOUR READERS ALREADY UNDERSTAND THAT ART IS IMPORTANT. YOU DON'T NEED TO BEGIN WITH SUCH A BROAD SET OF ASSERTIONS.

WHAT "DIFFERENT PEOPLE" WILL YOU BE TALKING ABOUT IN THIS ESSAY?

WELL, A LOT OF CAVE PAINTINGS COME FROM CULTURES OF HUNTERS AND GATHERERS.

I GUESS MY INSTRUCTOR WANTS ME TO FOCUS ON **THEIR** IDEAS...

OK, GOOD. WHAT IDEAS?

PREHISTORIC ART

Since the dawn of time, art has made the expression of ideas and feelings possible. This makes art a hugely important part of all human life. Art even appears in caves that were visited by ancient humans, and art remains an important part of basically every culture everywhere around the globe. Different people have different ideas about what makes art important or valuable, and about why works of art like cave paintings were created in the first place and how they can best be preserved for future generations. But many people agree that art is one of the ingredients that contributes to making life worth living. In this essay, I will examine the views of several important art historians about cave art and analyze where I stand on these questions.

HMM. WHAT IDEAS WOULD BE IMPORTANT TO THAT KIND OF CULTURE?

MAYBE I SHOULD SPECULATE ON WHY SO MANY CAVE ARTISTS CHOSE TO SHOW IMAGES OF **ANIMALS**-- BUT NOT **PEOPLE.**

AND IMAGES OF **REAL** CAVE ART WOULD BE A BETTER WAY TO ILLUSTRATE MY ARGUMENT.

I REALLY THINK YOU'RE ON TO SOMETHING INTERESTING --

-- AND PROBABLY GETTING CLOSER TO WHAT YOUR INSTRUCTOR IS ASKING YOU TO THINK ABOUT.

I COULD START BY FOCUSING ON IMAGES OF BISON, WHICH WERE IMPORTANT AS FOOD.

BISON PROVIDED HIDES, TOO, AND EVEN THEIR BONES COULD BE MADE INTO TOOLS. BISON WERE A BIG PART OF THAT CULTURE.

THAT SOUNDS LIKE A MUCH BETTER START-ING POINT.

OK, I'VE GOT SOME **REVISING** TO DO...

...I THINK I SEE THIS WHOLE THING IN A **NEW WAY!**

COMING UP IN THE NEXT EXCITING EPISODE OF **REFRAME**

"How does this LOOK?"

[pg 311]

DRAWING CONCLUSIONS

The following assignments ask you to
think about your revision process.

1 List the best and worst revision advice you've ever received. You might consider your experiences revising writing or essays, photoshopping images, creating graphic designs, or even developing a piece of art or craft work.

Next, draft a set of "best practices for responding to my work," and turn it into a publishable format and genre that you can distribute to the next person you share your work with. You might write a letter, create a wallet-sized "peer response guide," design an infographic, or create a short video or Web site whose URL you can hand out.

2 Create a reverse outline of an essay by highlighting the thesis statement and writing one-sentence summaries of the key argument each paragraph makes. Write down what you know about the author and the audience for the essay.

Next, create "characters" out of the author and an audience member. Write a short dialogue in which the author tries to convince the audience member of his or her claim using only the one-sentence paragraph summaries as arguments. Is your audience character convinced? If not, what argument points fall flat, or what additional information does the author character need to provide? Does the audience character introduce new counterarguments that your author character might need to address?

3

Maxine Hong Kingston was once forced to radically and dramatically revise a draft of her novel after it was burned in a house fire. Fortunately, there are less tragic and more controlled ways to simulate this sort of revision.

Print out your essay, read through it, and then seal it in an envelope. Walk away for a short break, and when you get back to your work space, try to reconstruct the essay from memory. Print out that version, unseal the envelope, and compare the two drafts.

Choose the best parts from each draft, and weave them together to make an improved, revised draft.

4

Choose one paragraph, from your own writing or from something you're reading, and take inventory of the contents: Are the sentences mostly long or short? Are there more simple, compound, or complex sentences in the paragraph?

Then rewrite the paragraph a few different ways. Combine sentences so that all the sentences are long. How does that change the experience of reading the paragraph? Is it more or less accessible to the reader? Does it change the tone of the piece?

Next, rewrite the paragraph using only short and simple sentences. What effect does that change have on the text? Keep experimenting with a number of variables: rewriting from a different perspective (from third-person to first-person, for instance), rewriting with all active or all passive voice sentences, and so on. Write a brief analysis of the effects of each change.

LAUNCHING INTO THE FUTURE OF GENRES

BEFORE WE TALK ABOUT PUTTING WORK IN FRONT OF AN AUDIENCE, WE THOUGHT WE'D TAKE A LITTLE BREAK FROM WRITING.

WE BOTH ENJOY FILM A GREAT DEAL.

DRAMA, COMEDY, ROMANCE, HORROR, WESTERN, SCIENCE FICTION, ACTION/ADVENTURE, MYSTERY, THRILLER...

THERE ARE MANY DIFFERENT CATEGORIES TO CHOOSE FROM.

AUDIENCES EXPECT DIFFERENT THINGS FROM DIFFERENT GENRES.

AND EACH GENRE IS A UNIQUE EXPERIENCE, WITH DIFFERENT CONVENTIONS AND EXPECTATIONS.

HEY--

I THOUGHT WE WERE SEEING A SCIENCE FICTION FILM TODAY...

...BUT I'M IN THE MOOD FOR A ROMANTIC COMEDY.

AS YOU CAN SEE, GENRE OFTEN SETS THE STAGE IN DETERMINING HOW AUDIENCES WILL APPROACH A FILM -- OR A PIECE OF WRITING.

UH-OH.

HELP!

FOR INSTANCE, THE GENRE OF SCIENCE FICTION MIGHT EVOKE OUTER SPACE, NON-HUMAN CREATURES, OR LIFE IN A HIGH-TECH FUTURE.

WE LEARN THE CONVENTIONS OF DIFFERENT GENRES AS WE'RE EXPOSED TO THEM.

HUMAN F

BEAM

WE'RE USED TO CATEGORIZING FILM ACCORDING TO GENRE, BUT GENRE IS AT WORK **EVERYWHERE**.

BOOT!

DIFFERENT GENRES CALL FOR DIFFERENT RHETORICAL CHOICES.

EVERYTHING WE SEE -- FROM WORD CHOICE TO DESIGN -- TELLS US WHAT TO EXPECT.

AUDIENCES FOR A NEWSMAGAZINE EXPECT TRUSTWORTHY STORIES NOT INFLUENCED BY ADVERTISERS.

SO IT'S IMPORTANT FOR THE STORIES TO BE DESIGNED DIFFERENTLY FROM THE ADS.

BUT IN A SCIENCE FICTION MAGAZINE...

...TELLING THE ADS FROM THE ARTICLES PROBABLY DOESN'T MATTER AS MUCH TO READERS.

AN ANALYSIS OF A **POEM**, IN CONTRAST...

...MIGHT NOT BEGIN WITH A SEPARATE BACKGROUND SECTION, BUT THE WRITER MIGHT BRING UP INFORMATION ABOUT THE POET'S LIFE OR OTHER CONTEXT WHEN ANALYZING PARTICULAR LINES.

PROVIDING THAT KIND OF INFORMATION IS A WAY FOR THE WRITER TO AN-NOUNCE A PARTICULAR APPROACH TO INTERPRETATION.

HEY!

GORGO! NO!

SO, THERE'S A **METHOD** EVEN IN THE MADNESS OF POETRY ANALYSIS!

DESIGN

MEDIUM

SUBJECT MATTER

TONE

FORMAT

CHOICE

LEVEL of LANGUAGE

BUT THE FORMATS OF A LITERARY ANALYSIS AND A LAB REPORT WILL TYPICALLY BE VERY DIFFERENT.

SOME GENRES THAT ARE DESIGNED FOR PARTICULAR PURPOSES AND AUDIENCES...

...MAY SEEM PRETTY ALIEN TO OUTSIDERS.

HELP!

AND WHILE EACH OF THESE WRITING SPACES -- EMAIL, WEB PAGES, TEXTS -- CAN HAVE ITS OWN GENRE CONVENTIONS, EACH CAN ALSO ACCOMMODATE A WIDE VARIETY OF GENRES.

FOR EXAMPLE, BLOGS AND WIKIS ARE WEB GENRES THAT ARE ALSO COLLABORATIVE WRITING SPACES.

LIZ IS THE PRIMARY AUTHOR OF HER BLOG, *VIRTUALPOLITIK*, AND JONATHAN CAN MAKE COMMENTS.

ARTICLES ON WIKIPEDIA OFTEN HAVE MORE THAN ONE PRIMARY AUTHOR.

BARGE IN!

IN EACH CASE, THE GENRE ESTABLISHES EXPECTATIONS FOR HOW PEOPLE SHOULD CONVERSE ON THE SITE.

WHAT HAPPENS WHEN A BOOK BECOMES A FILM?

OR A TELEVISION SHOW BECOMES A VIDEO GAME?

WHAT DOES *PUBLISHING* MEAN, ANYWAY?

ENTERING THE FINAL FRONTIER WITH PUBLICATION

NO MATTER WHAT THE MEDIUM, GENRE IS ABOUT JOINING A CONVERSATION AND UNDERSTANDING THE RULES OF THAT CONVERSATION.

YOU CAN THINK OF GENRE AS THE STRUCTURE, THE SPACE OF CONVENTIONS, THROUGH WHICH WE COMMUNICATE OUR OWN IDEAS, IN CONVERSATION WITH OTHERS.

THROUGHOUT THIS BOOK, WE HAVE BEEN TALKING ABOUT WRITING AS A KIND OF SPACE -- A SPACE IN WHICH WE CAN MAKE ALL SORTS OF THINGS HAPPEN.

WE'VE SEEN WRITING "TAKE SHAPE" IN A VARIETY OF FORMS, THROUGH A VARIETY OF GENRES...

...AND IN A VARIETY OF MEDIA, INCLUDING BOTH DIGITAL MEDIA AND OLD-SCHOOL TECHNOLOGIES, LIKE PEN AND PAPER.

TURBO STUFF

NOW, WE'D LIKE TO -- AHEM! -- SHIFT GEARS, AS IT WERE.

HYPER-WARP DRIVE 3000

BECAUSE WHILE WRITING EXISTS IN MANY **SPACES**...

...IT ALSO **MOVES.**

IT CHANGES SHAPE, FORM, AND FUNCTION DEPENDING ON WHAT WE'RE COMMUNICATING, TO WHOM, AND HOW.

SOMETIMES SIMILAR IDEAS MAY BE PUBLISHED IN VERY DIFFERENT KINDS OF WORK.

ERRI

WHOA, IT'S **GREG BENFORD**, ACADEMIC PHYSICIST AND SCIENCE FICTION WRITER!

HE'S WRITTEN ABOUT THE GALACTIC CENTER IN NOVELS AND ALSO IN ACADEMIC PAPERS.

BUT *PUBLISHING* JUST MEANS GOING PUBLIC WITH YOUR WORK, AND YOU DON'T NEED TO BE A BOOK AUTHOR TO EXPERIENCE THAT THRILL.

SHWOOSH!!!

YIKES!

THANK YOU!

WRITING MORPHS AND CHANGES MEANING AS IT MOVES FROM ONE MEDIUM OR GENRE OR RHETORICAL SITUATION TO ANOTHER.

YOU'VE SEEN THIS MOVEMENT AS YOU'VE TRAVELED WITH US THROUGH THE COURSE OF THIS BOOK.

AND WRITING MOVES TOWARD AUDIENCES -- SOMETIMES SPECIFIC AND INTENDED AUDIENCES, AND SOMETIMES UNINTENDED AUDIENCES.

AS WRITING GETS **READ**, OTHER PEOPLE CAN RESPOND.

A HIGH-SPEED EXCHANGE OF INFORMATION CAN BE THRILLING...

...WITH DIGITAL GENRES MAKING NEW FORMS OF AUTHORSHIP AVAILABLE TO WRITERS WHO MIGHT NEVER FIND AUDIENCES OTHERWISE...

305

...AND WITH INFORMATION DISSEMINATED AS QUICKLY AS IT IS PRODUCED AND CONSUMED--

WAIT, WERE YOU SPEEDING?

IT'S TRUE, MY FRIENDS.

TEXTUAL AND VISUAL MATERIAL IS CONSTANTLY ON THE MOVE...

...BEING RETASKED AND REPURPOSED FOR A VARIETY OF MEDIA...

...BUT YOU HAVE TO PAY ATTENTION TO WHAT YOU'RE DOING, OR YOU'LL END UP PULLED OVER TO THE SIDE OF THE INFORMATION SUPERHIGHWAY.

YES INDEED, YOU HAVE TO PLOT YOUR COURSE CAREFULLY...

...AND MAKE SURE ALL THE GEARS OF YOUR MEDIUM AND MESSAGE FIT TOGETHER PERFECTLY, SO THAT YOUR WRITING DOESN'T...

...UHHH...

...ROCKET OFF IN THE WRONG DIRECTION...

bits

All Places > The English Community

Bedford Bits

Actions ▾ ⓘ

Overview Content Images People Subspaces

All Places > The English Community > Bedford Bits > Blog > Blog Posts

Learning to See Writing

🖹 Blog Post created by **Jonathan Alexander** 🔖 on Nov 7, 2016

[For] me, one of the biggest challenges of working on a graphic book has been adapting to thinking and composing in a different [med]ium. Indeed, one of the lessons we have learned in the process is that we can't just think like "text" authors; we also have to begin to [think vi]sually. As we sketch out the chapters, panel by panel, we try to provide detailed visual cues for Kevin Cannon and Zander Cannon, [fab]ulous artists–who, in turn, not only modify our initial image directions and augment them beautifully, but have also challenged how [we und]erstand and use text in the graphic book form.

[Along] these lines, one of the earliest lessons we learned about our use of text is that we were initially relying too much [on] captioning and not enough on dialogue to carry the instructional weight of each chapter. That is, we were thinking [li]ke the text-producing scholars that we are, and not like the collaborative graphic authors we needed to be. We were constantly explaining rhetorical concepts, for instance, while ignoring how images and dialogue—the principal features [o]f the comic form—could be used to convey our ideas about writing. Comparing initial drafts of the first several chapters with their more recent revisions shows a steady move away from captioning to significantly more reliance on [dialogue] [and] [im]as.

[Concom]itant with that shift has been a shift in how we think about the project and the pr[ocess] [to] [ma]ximize our use of the comic form. For instance, we've frequently found ourselv[es] [read]ing dialogue out loud to make sure that our characters strike the right—and cred[ible] [The dialog]ue format forced us to focus on the process of understanding rhetorical conce[pts] [in] [ac]tion, coming to understand concepts such as logos and ethos, or the complexi[ty] [of a writing proc]ess. The format of the comic book allows us—actually requires us—to model, d[ifferent] [way]ns to compose.

[I focus] on this particular example of how our composing process had to shift because it seems t[o] [offer] [a good] reminder of how different genres call forth different modalities of thinking, as Anis Bawarshi argues in *Genre and* [th]e *Invention of the Writer* :

(Photo) Mack McCoy

REFRAME with Luis & Cindy

How does this LOOK?

HEY, LUIS.
HEY, CINDY!
HEY, CINDY'S MOM!

ISN'T THIS MEDIA LAB AWESOME?

YEAH, I'M DOING MORE AND MORE MEDIA PROJECTS FOR MY CLASSES, SO IT'S NICE TO HAVE ALL THIS SOFTWARE...

SO, WHAT ARE YOU GUYS UP TO?

I'M HELPING MY MOM LEARN TO MAKE PRE-SENTATION SLIDES.

SHE'S WORKING ON A PROJECT FOR HER WRITING CLASS.

COMPUTERS AREN'T MY THING, BUT I'M ACTUALLY HAVING A GOOD TIME ANYWAY...

YEAH, I'M WORKING ON A PRESENTATION TOO... FOR MY RESEARCH PROJECT ON FORCED MIGRATION.

I'M WRITING ABOUT PEOPLE WHO COME TO THE UNITED STATES BE-CAUSE THEIR LIVES ARE IN DANGER IN THEIR HOME COUNTRIES.

HEY, REMEMBER HOW I TOLD YOU THAT MY MOTHER LEFT VIETNAM AS A BOAT PERSON?

SHE CAME TO THIS COUNTRY BECAUSE OF FORCED MIGRATION.

HER UNCLE HAD ALREADY BEEN EXECUTED BY THE COMMUNISTS. HER OLDER BROTHER HAD BEEN A TRANSLATOR FOR THE U.S. MILITARY, SO THE WHOLE FAMILY HAD TO LEAVE.

I ALWAYS TELL MY DAUGHTER HOW LUCKY SHE IS.

I LIVED IN A REFUGEE CAMP WHEN I WAS HER AGE!

HMM...

REC

WOULD YOU MIND IF I INTERVIEWED YOU FOR MY PROJECT?

IT WOULD BE GREAT TO HAVE AN EYEWITNESS REPORT!

AND SO...

BUT HOW WILL YOU INCLUDE A VIDEO IN YOUR PAPER?

WELL...

...FOR OUR RESEARCH PROJECTS, WE HAVE TO WRITE A PAPER AND THEN CREATE A MULTIMEDIA PRESENTATION ON THE SAME SUBJECT.

LIZ WANTS US TO CHOOSE A SPECIFIC CASE STUDY, SO I COULD WRITE ABOUT FORCED MIGRATION FROM VIETNAM TO THE UNITED STATES.

Forced Migration Online: Resources f
Ongoing Study and Research

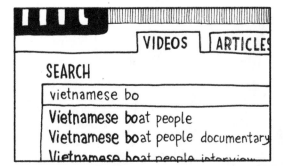

SEARCH

vietnamese bo

Vietnamese boat people
Vietnamese boat people documentary
Vietnamese boat people interview

BY THE END OF THE TERM, WE HAVE TO COMBINE ALL OUR WORK INTO ONE COHERENT PROJECT...

...SO I THINK I'M GOING TO MAKE A WEB SITE WHERE I CAN POST MY PAPER ON VIETNAMESE REFUGEES AND ALSO LINK TO VIDEO AND IMAGES AND DOCUMENTS THAT I COLLECT.

AN INTERVIEW CAN BE A REALLY POWERFUL SOURCE.

CAROL, WOULD YOU TALK ABOUT WHAT IT FELT LIKE TO LIVE THROUGH FORCED MIGRATION?

I'D BE FLATTERED TO BE INCLUDED.

GREAT!

I'LL THINK OF SOME QUESTIONS, AND THEN WE CAN GET STARTED...

RESEARCH!

WRITE!

INTERVIEW!

EDIT!

315

ONE WEEK LATER...

LUIS?

DID MY MOM EMAIL YOU?

NO. WHY?

CHECK OUT THE COMMENTS ON THAT VIDEO YOU DID FOR YOUR PROJECT.

Comments

Reply

Usanmez FORENER GO HOME!

Reply

MOM WAS PRETTY UPSET.

SHE WANTED TO EMAIL YOU TO TAKE DOWN THE VIDEO, BUT SHE KNOWS IT'S IMPORTANT FOR YOUR PROJECT.

Disable Comments

CLICK

I CAN'T BELIEVE THE TERRIBLE THINGS PEOPLE WRITE IN ONLINE COMMENTS SOMETIMES.

IT'S LIKE THEY FORGET THEY'RE TALKING TO OTHER HUMAN BEINGS.

TELL ME ABOUT IT.

I'M REALLY SORRY THIS HAPPENED, BUT I'M GLAD YOU TOLD ME.

I'M DELETING THE COMMENT.

MAYBE I SHOULD EVEN MAKE THE VIDEO PRIVATE.

THAT'S NICE OF YOU...

BUT...

BUT WHAT?

I DUNNO... I'M SORRY MOM WAS UPSET, BUT IT SEEMS LIKE **CENSORSHIP** TO DELETE THE COMMENT.

REALLY!?!

I CAN'T BELIEVE YOU'D SAY THAT.

I KNOW, BUT THOSE VIEWS ARE OUT THERE... AND HIDING THEM WON'T MAKE THEM GO AWAY.

I THINK I'M GOING TO MENTION THIS INCIDENT IN MY INTRODUCTION, IF THAT'S OKAY WITH YOUR MOTHER.

LET ME EMAIL HER SO WE CAN TALK ABOUT IT.

ANOTHER WEEK LATER...

HEY, LUIS, CHECK THIS OUT.

MY MOM WENT TO THE MEDIA LAB AND MADE HER OWN VIDEO TO RESPOND TO THE COMMENT ABOUT HER INTERVIEW!

I KNOW THAT MY ADOPTED HOME, THE UNITED STATES, ENCOURAGES FREEDOM OF SPEECH...

...AND I'M DELIGHTED THAT BEING AN AMERICAN GIVES ME THE RIGHT TO TALK BACK TO THOSE WHO QUESTION MY CONTRIBUTIONS TO THIS COUNTRY...

WOW! GOOD FOR HER!

I KNOW. SHE ACTUALLY ROCKS SOMETIMES.

HIGH-FIVE!

NOW YOU CAN POST THE ORIGINAL VIDEO WITH BOTH THE ANGRY COMMENT AND HER VIDEO RESPONSE...

...LIKE A **DIALOGUE** -- BUT ONE THAT MAKES A REALLY EFFECTIVE ARGUMENT!

ha ha ha

YOU KNOW MY MOM -- SHE ALWAYS GETS THE LAST WORD!

ha ha ha ha ha ha ha

317

DRAWING CONCLUSIONS

The following assignments ask you to think
about making your work available to audiences.

1 Choose an activity in which you're an expert -- a hobby, sport, craft, skill, or something else. Take notes about the activity: steps/processes, necessary materials,
favorite memories, emotional responses, motivations for sticking with it, etc.
Using your notes, draft a short poem about the activity. Then draft a short
how-to tutorial about doing that same thing. Finally, compare the two texts
and the experiences of writing in two different genres about the same topic.

Do the different genres speak to different audiences?
Do they serve the same purposes? Do they use the
same rhetorical strategies? Does your "voice," or
the way you use your identity as an author, shift
between the two genres? Why or why not?

2 Reflect on some of the research papers you've written in the past.
What materials did you need, and what steps did you need to take
to successfully complete them? Drawing from these experiences,
write a "recipe for a successful research paper." List the necessary
ingredients and quantities, and include detailed steps, in order, to
ensure that a reader can follow your recipe. Look at some examples
of recipes, and consider including a brief introductory blurb about the
finished product, notes on appropriate pairings with this "dish," pro tips
or warnings, or even step-by-step photos.

Does the recipe genre work for giving directions for completing a piece of
writing? Why or why not? Did your recipe function as a serious set of directions or something else? How do the tone and purpose of your "recipe for a
successful research paper" compare to those of a more conventional recipe?

3

Book trailers, short videos made by fans of books and published on YouTube, take the genre of the movie trailer and adapt it to generate excitement around a literary text. Part endorsement, part teaser, and part book report, book trailers serve as winks to fans or invitations to join a community of readers.

Spend some time checking out book trailers for books you may already love and books you may not be familiar with. Then, choose a book that you've recently read, and sketch out a storyboard for your own book trailer. What elements of the trailer must you include to make the genre recognizable to other viewers? What is the primary "message" and purpose of your trailer? For whom is your trailer designed? How have you communicated the essence of the book -- its genre, tone, and subject matter -- to your audience?

4

This chapter describes some ways that "going public" online can mean reaching unintended audiences, facing unforeseen consequences, or receiving unpleasant or unproductive feedback. Liz and Jonathan feel strongly that developing an awareness of both the advantages and the risks of publishing digital media is important for everyone.

Fables and fairy tales are short fictional forms that are intended to teach lessons to young people. After doing some research on these genres, draft a fable or fairy tale teaching the next generation (younger relatives or neighbors, for example) about using the Internet responsibly.

GLOSSARY

INDEX

GLOSSARY

Analysis
A close examination of the parts of a text with the goal of interpreting it as a whole.

Argument
The primary purpose of a text, or the main claim it makes.

Assertion
A debatable claim.

Audience
The intended or accidental recipients of a communication.

Cause and effect
Tracing the reasons that led to an outcome, or anticipating the likely result of an event or circumstance.

Citation
The way the original source of a quotation, summary, or paraphrase is documented.

Comparison and contrast
Noting similarities and differences between two texts.

Composition
Creating a text in one or more media.

Conclusion
The end of a text that ties together its argument.

Context
The situation in which a text is created, including its creator, audience, purpose, medium, and genre, as well as other factors.

Credibility
The characteristic that makes a text believable.

Critical lens
A perspective or theoretical approach that provides a context for analysis.

Critical reading
An analytical approach to a text.

Discourse
Written or spoken communication, often characterized by its use in particular communities.

Ethos
The credibility or authority that a speaker or writer brings to a subject.

Evidence
The information used to support an argument.

Explication
Revealing or uncovering ideas that are not directly stated in a text.

Genre
A conventional format for presenting information and ideas.

Implicit messages
Ideas that are present in a text but not directly stated.

Integration
Weaving material from others' work into one's own text and adding commentary that explains the material's purpose and importance.

Interpretation
Using context and critical analysis to explain the meaning of a text.

Invention
Any technique (such as freewriting or brainstorming) for exploring new thoughts and ideas during the writing process.

Kairos
Awareness of the appropriate timing, occasion, or opportunity for a given rhetorical act.

Logos
Appeals to reason and logic in a text.

Medium (*plural*, Media)
Material that records, displays, stores, or spreads information.

Paraphrase
A detailed explanation of the contents of a source that rephrases the language of the original source.

Pathos
Appeals to emotion.

Peer revision *or* Peer review
The process of seeking feedback on a text from a classmate, colleague, or friend.

Plagiarism
Presenting the work of another as one's own, whether accidentally or deliberately.

Primary source
A work that presents a firsthand account of an event or a time.

Purpose
The aim of a communication.

Quotation
Direct repetition of material from a source.

Reflection
In writing, an analysis of a completed project that considers what the writer learned during the writing process.

Remediation
Revising a text that appeared originally in one medium so that it is effective in another medium.

Revision
The process of rewriting to improve a text, often by viewing it from different perspectives.

Rhetoric
The practice or study of effective communication.

Rhetorical analysis
Examining how, what, and why a given text communicates.

Secondary source
A work that describes, analyzes, or interprets a firsthand account or original work.

Summary
A brief, general restatement of the content of a source.

Surface errors
Distracting mistakes in grammar, punctuation, or spelling.

Synthesis
Putting information from multiple sources together to make one unified meaning.

Text
In rhetorical terms, any communication in any medium—including print books, films, Web content, slide presentations, Facebook posts, and so on.

Thesis
The main idea that a text develops.

Tone
The attitude that a text conveys to an audience.

Visual literacy
The ability to analyze elements of a visual text.

Voice
In writing, the way a writer expresses the person behind the words.

Writing process
The steps writers take in composing a text, which can vary greatly from writer to writer and from situation to situation.

INDEX